MAGIC
MUSHROOM
GROWER'S GUIDE

Simple Steps to Bulk Cultivation

Principium Quaesitor

TPS

www.magicmushroomgrowguide.com

Magic Mushroom Grower's Guide Simple Steps to Bulk Cultivation
Published by The Psychonautical Society
Copyright © 2015 Principium Quaesitor

First Printing: May, 2015
First Edition: May, 2015

ISBN-10: 0-9925584-0-9
ISBN-13: 978-0-9925584-0-6

National Library of Australia Cataloguing-in-Publication entry
Principium Quaesitor, author.
Magic mushroom grower's guide simple steps to bulk cultivation / Principium Quaesitor.

ISBN: 9780992558406 (paperback)
Mushrooms, Hallucinogenic--Growth.
Mushrooms, Hallucinogenic--Handbooks, manuals, etc.
579.616

The universe is a womb for the genesis of gods.

Contents

CHAPTER 8 ▪ Additional Resources 151

Preface

Psilocybin mushrooms have been part of human culture since earliest recorded history. Wall paintings dating from the Neolithic period found at the Tassili n'Ajjer plateau in Algeria depict the use of mushrooms in shamanistic rituals. Mayan and Aztec civilizations used psilocybin mushrooms for purposes of religion, divination, and healing in pre-Columbian times, and their descendants continue to do so today. In his book *Food of the Gods,* Terence McKenna proposed that psychedelic mushrooms may have even played a role in human evolution by stimulating brain activity and acting as a catalyst for the development of language, arts, and religious impulses. It seems that psilocybin mushrooms have influenced and shaped our perceptions from the earliest stages of human history.

In modern times, psilocybin mushrooms continue to be a potent tool for understanding ourselves and the world around us. At this time in history, technological innovation is increasing at an unprecedented rate. Advances in computing, information technology, medical science and nanotechnology over the coming decades will drastically change the way we live. It has been theorized that a point of "technological singularity" is approaching, when artificial intelligence will surpass human intelligence. Faced with such momentous, paradigm-shifting events, mankind will be forced to consider its place and purpose in the universe more deeply than ever before. Psychedelics and the unique awareness they engender are indispensable as far as how they are able to aid in this analysis. Psilocybin mushrooms are one of our most ancient tools in this regard, and they have the potential to aid us further in realizing our fullest cognitive, spiritual, and physical potentials.

In this context—and for the purpose of disseminating essential information—this book presents a methodology for inexpensive, effective, bulk cultivation of the psilocybin mushroom *Psilocybe cubensis*. Probably the most well-known psychedelic mushroom in the world, *P. cubensis* can be found growing in natural settings in North and South America, South Asia, Southeast Asia, and Australia and has been cultivated in home settings since the publication of growing techniques in the 1970s. The book *Psilocybin: Magic Mushroom Grower's Guide* by O.T. Oss and O.N. Oeric was one of the first books to describe accessible and affordable cultivation methods for *P. cubensis*. More recent publications like *The Mushroom Cultivator* and *Growing Gourmet and Medicinal Mushrooms* by mycologist Paul Stamets have become essential references for hobbyists and professional mycologists alike.

Magic Mushroom Grower's Guide Simple Steps to Bulk Cultivation outlines every step in the simplest bulk-cultivation process. Information is presented in a logical progression with step-by-step guides, along with accompanying essential theory. Hundreds of images and diagrams throughout the book clarify instructions and show the stunning results that are possible. In addition to providing basic information for the beginner, the book also covers advanced cultivation methods and construction of advanced equipment, thus allowing rapid progression beyond the basic method of growing from a spore print.

Principium Quaesitor
The Psychonautical Society

CHAPTER 1

Overview

Mushroom cultivation is a fun and rewarding pastime. You don't need to be a trained mycologist to grow mushrooms; all you need is the right equipment, an understanding of the process, an inquiring mind, and a little patience. Growing mushrooms will teach you firsthand about the life cycle of fungi and the role of fungi in ecosystems. Along your journey, you will undoubtedly develop a deep appreciation for nature, not to mention an enhanced perception of the universe and your place in it. A special sense of pride and achievement comes with growing your own source of mind-expanding psychedelics.

Mushroom cultivation basically involves nurturing and feeding mushroom mycelium, and then coaxing it to produce fruit. The grower aims to create optimal growing conditions by providing suitable substrate materials and regulating various environmental conditions, such as cycling of gases and the availability of moisture, temperature, and light. In addition, the grower must take steps to keep contaminating microbes from interfering.

From first inoculations to harvest, the growing process involves stages of activity followed by periods of watching and waiting. The simplest bulk-growing process is as follows: Spores are scraped from a spore print into sterilized water, and then drawn into a syringe. This spore solution is introduced to a sterile grain medium, a process referred to as *inoculation*. Spores germinate and form white mushroom mycelium, which grows on— and eventually completely colonizes—the grain medium. Colonized grain is then mixed with another growing medium, referred to as *bulk substrate*, and allowed to undergo an additional period of colonization, thus expanding the volume of mycelia available. The colonized bulk substrate is then induced to produce mushrooms, which are harvested. This basic process of growing from a spore print is represented visually in the diagram below.

Inoculations, and subsequent crops of mushrooms that originate from a spore print, are referred to as *multispore inoculations*, or *multispore grows*. The term "multispore" reflects the fact that mycelium grown from a spore print has originated from multiple spores. Limitations associated with multispore growing, and an alternative approach of growing from tissue cultures using agar, are discussed in detail in chapter 7.

Mushroom cultivation requires various specialized equipment. Some equipment can be constructed from household materials or purchased inexpensively from a hardware store. Other niche materials and equipment may require a little more detective work to track down. Advice for sourcing materials and equipment can be found in chapter 8.

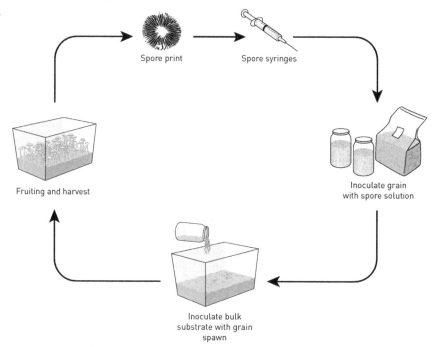

Basic process of growing from a spore print

CHAPTER 2

Aseptic Technique

Key stages of the growing process must be conducted in sterile conditions. Contamination can completely ruin a mushroom grow, resulting in wasted time and a loss of materials. Therefore, our first goal is to learn how to work in sterile conditions to minimize the risk of contamination that could potentially disrupt a successful grow. The methods we use to create a sterile work space—and to prevent contaminants from entering that space—are referred to collectively as the *aseptic technique.*

Not all stages of the growing operation require sterile conditions. From the moment colonized grain is mixed with bulk substrate, the remainder of the grow operation occurs in nonsterile, open-air conditions.

Key Equipment and Methods

Agar and Petri Dishes
Agar is a growing medium used to culture mushroom mycelium for the purpose of cloning and strain isolation. Agar is sterilized in a pressure cooker, and then poured into petri dishes and allowed to set.

Disposable Gloves
Gloves prevent contaminants on our skin from coming into contact with equipment and the work area. Gloves should be repeatedly wiped with 70 percent isopropanol during sterile procedures.

Isopropyl Alcohol (isopropanol)
Diluted to 70 percent with water, isopropanol is used as a disinfectant to sterilize surfaces, equipment, and gloved hands. Isopropanol is dispensed from a squeeze bottle or spray bottle, or applied to a paper towel and then wiped over the target surface.

Laboratory Coat

A laboratory coat is always worn during sterile procedures to prevent contaminants that could be on our skin and everyday clothes from entering the work space. Arms should always be covered when working in a SAB. Alternatively, a freshly laundered, long-sleeve shirt, or Tyvek sleeves, can be worn in place of a laboratory coat.

Laminar Flow Hood

A laminar flow hood is used to create a localized sterile area free of airborne contaminants. A blower or fan delivers a continuous air current through a high-efficiency filter capable of removing fine particles and contaminants from the air. The resulting downstream airflow is free of contaminating aerosols, thus providing a sterile area to work in.

Pressure Cooker

A large pressure cooker / canner is used to sterilize equipment and grow media, such as grains and agar. The pressure cooker is operated at 15 psi for a duration of anywhere between thirty minutes to two hours, depending on the materials being treated. The temperature inside the pressure cooker can reach 121°C (250°F), thus providing an effective means of sterilization.

Spirit Burner

A spirit burner is used to flame-sterilize metal equipment, such as a spore-syringe needle or scalpel blade, before the equipment comes into contact with sterile media.

Still-air Box (SAB)

Made from a large plastic tub, the still-air box (SAB) provides an enclosed work space protected from drafts and airborne contaminants. The interior is wiped clean with 70 percent isopropanol and loaded with necessary equipment. Sterile procedures are performed inside the SAB by accessing the interior via two armholes on one side.

The Work Space

A suitable work space is required for sterile procedures. The work space requires a flat area, such as a bench or desk. A laminate, or similar surface, is perfect, because it allows for easy cleaning. Air currents are a major source of contamination; therefore, ideally, the work space should be in a room that isn't drafty, and can be closed off from the rest of the house. Having a water outlet close by is also an advantage. A laundry bench makes an ideal location. A SAB, or flow hood, is used for key procedures to provide added protection against airborne contaminants.

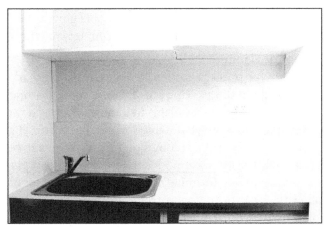
A suitable work space for sterile procedures

Before conducting any sterile procedures, you should prepare the work space according to the following steps:

1. Make sure you are wearing a laboratory coat or freshly laundered clothes, including a long-sleeved shirt or Tyvek sleeves to cover your arms.

2. While wearing disposable gloves, use a paper towel soaked in 70 percent isopropanol to wipe down all the surfaces around the work area, including the bench top, adjacent walls, and the undersides of any overhanging shelves.

3. Close any doors or windows that could allow drafts into the room.

4. Sterilize and prepare equipment. Equipment can be wrapped in foil and sterilized in a pressure cooker before use.

   Items are arranged within easy reach on the bench top or inside the SAB. Small implements (e.g., scalpels, syringes, and spoons) can be arranged on a pad of paper towels soaked in 70 percent isopropanol.

   Scalpel blades and syringe tips are flame-sterilized immediately before use by holding the equipment to a flame for five seconds until the portion held to the flame glows red. The spirit burner is placed on the workbench outside the SAB. Metal implements are flame-sterilized and then brought inside the SAB for use. The spirit burner should be positioned far away from any isopropanol cleaning supplies.

   Note that boiling equipment in water isn't effective against certain bacterial and fungal spores, and, therefore, doesn't provide 100-percent sterilization. As such, boiling is not a recommended method for equipment sterilization purposes.

5. Before starting work, don a fresh pair of disposable gloves, then wipe them thoroughly with paper towel soaked in 70 percent isopropanol.

Pressure Cooker or Canner

The pressure cooker (or pressure canner) is an essential piece of equipment. It will be used throughout the growing process to sterilize growing media and equipment. Pressure cookers are available in a range of sizes; however, small-capacity electric appliances aren't suitable for our purposes. High-capacity, stove-top models that allow large volumes of growing media to be processed at a time are required. The term "canner" is reserved for large pressure cookers designed for food preserving (canning). Canners are perfect for our needs.

Always follow the basic operating instructions that come with your specific pressure cooker or pressure canner. Take care to monitor the water level in your cooker or canner. A good portion will be lost when the water turns to steam during operation, and this water needs to be replaced if you are treating successive batches of growing media or equipment. If the water boils off completely, the pressure cooker can overheat and warp, causing potential damage to the materials inside.

23-qt Presto pressure cooker

If we use the example of a 23-qt Presto pressure cooker (pictured above), the basic operating procedure would be as follows:

1. Place 2.85 L (3 qt) of boiling water, the canning rack (comes with the cooker), and items into the pressure cooker.

2. Place the cover on the pressure cooker and turn it to the closed position.

3. Place the pressure cooker on the stove top. Heat the pressure cooker on a high setting until steam coming from the vent pipe is visible.

4. Place the pressure regulator on the vent pipe. As pressure builds, the air

vent/cover lock will lift, and lock the cover of the pressure cooker.

5. When the pressure cooker reaches 15 psi, the pressure regulator will lift slightly and rock, venting excess pressure to keep the pressure inside the cooker at an even 15 psi.

6. Start timing your countdown from the moment the pressure cooker reaches 15 psi.

7. Once the pressure cooker reaches 15 psi, you can turn the heat down marginally, but keep watch to ensure the pressure level doesn't drop below 15 psi. If it does drop below 15 psi, you will need to restart your countdown from the moment it heats back up to 15 psi.

8. When the time is up, turn off the burner. Allow the pressure to drop on its own accord. Don't try to remove the lid until the air vent/cover lock and the overpressure plug have dropped, and no steam escapes when the regulator is lifted.

Still-Air Box (SAB)

A SAB provides reliable protection against airborne contaminants, and can be made inexpensively from common materials. These attributes make it perfect for the beginner grower.

The interior of the SAB should always be cleaned before use. Paper towels soaked in 70 percent isopropanol are used to wipe the inside walls, corners, and base. Special care is given to clean the underside of the lid to prevent dust from dropping onto equipment or materials.

The interior of an SAB isn't considered a perfectly sterile environment because air can move freely into the SAB via the armholes. The role of the SAB is to provide added protection against airborne contaminants by further eliminating drafts in the work area.

When you work with the SAB, your movements should always be calm and methodical. Avoid making abrupt or rushed movements that could generate drafts, and blow around airborne contaminants. You should be wearing clean clothes, Tyvek sleeves, and disposable gloves when working inside the SAB. Wipe your gloved hands and Tyvek sleeves thoroughly with a paper towel soaked in 70 percent isopropanol before starting work.

The spirit burner is always placed on the workbench outside the SAB— never inside.

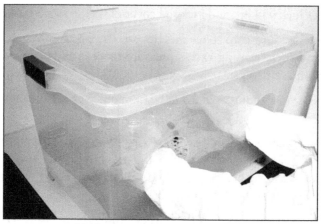

Making spore syringes inside a SAB

2.1 GUIDE: MAKING A STILL-AIR BOX (SAB)

Making a SAB involves cutting two armholes of approximately 12 cm (4.7 in) circumference in the side of a clear plastic tub. The armholes should be positioned shoulder-width apart. The chosen tub should have a clear, flat lid that allows good visibility into the interior. Lids that provide poor visibility can be customized with a sheet of clear acrylic. The tub should also have a decent amount of vertical space. A more spacious SAB is better for working with spawn bags and large batches of spawn jars.

Materials
- Clear plastic tub
- Drill with about a 12 cm (4–5 in) hole cutter or an adjustable circle cutter
- Sheet of clear acrylic (optional)
- Silicone (optional)

Method (see Figure 2.1)

1. On the side of the tub, mark two points a little wider than shoulder width apart (Figure 2.1A). These points represent the center point of each armhole.

2. Cut the armholes using the drill with an attached hole-cutter or circle cutter (Figure 2.1B). Apply firm pressure, but allow the tool to gradually do the work. The plastic can be brittle and may crack if you press too hard.

At this point, your SAB should be complete, provided you have a lid that allows for good visibility. If your lid is opaque, or does not allow for good visibility, follow the steps below to customize the lid with a sheet of clear acrylic.

3. If necessary, trim the acrylic sheet to the desired size. A jigsaw or circular saw is best for this task. Acrylic usually comes with protective paper wrapping. Make sure to leave this on while trimming due to the fact that acrylic scratches easily.

It is also possible to have the acrylic cut to size at the place of purchase. Therefore, if you don't have access to the above-mentioned power tools, this would be an alternative option.

4. Drill pilot holes into the lid (Figure 2.1C). Use a hacksaw blade or jigsaw to cut a rectangular section from the lid (Figure 2.1D).

5. Run a bead of silicone around the edge (Figure 2.1E). Next, press the acrylic sheet down onto the lid, ensuring good contact with the silicone all the way around (Figure 2.1F).

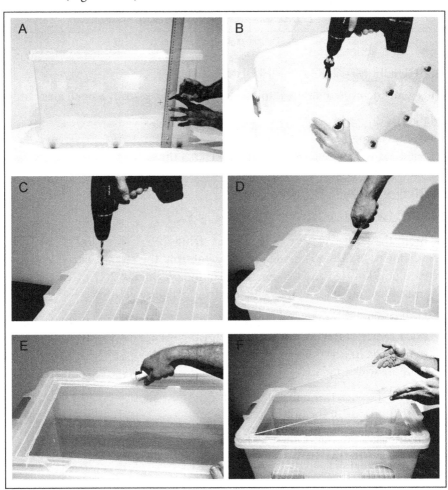

Figure 2.1. Making a still-air box

2.2 GUIDE: MAKING A SPIRIT BURNER

This guide demonstrates how to make a spirit burner from a small glass jar.

Materials
- Cotton string
- Small jar with a metal lid (a baby food jar is the perfect size)
- Fuel (methylated spirits/denatured alcohol, ethanol, or undiluted isopropanol are all suitable for use as fuel)

Method (see Figure 2.2)

1. Braid the wick. Weave two lengths of string into each strand of the braid as shown. Braiding is made easier by knotting the strands at one end and fixing the knotted end to something stationary (Figure 2.2A). Tease out the strands at both ends of the completed wick (Figure 2.2B).

2. Drill two holes into the metal jar lid (Figure 2.2C). Position one hole in the exact center of the lid, as this will be for the wick. Position the second hole to one side to serve as a vent. The central hole should provide a tight fit to hold the wick in place.

3. Thread the wick through the center hole. Allow about 1 cm (0.4 in) to show on the top side of the lid (Figure 2.2D).

4. Fill the jar a quarter of the way full with fuel, then fit the lid.

5. Allow the fuel to soak up through the wick before lighting. To speed up the process, cover the vent with your finger, and invert the jar once. To prevent evaporation, store unused fuel in an airtight container.

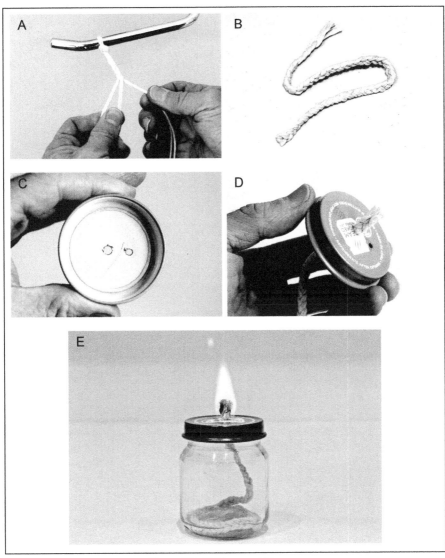

Figure 2.2. Making a spirit burner

CHAPTER 3

From Spores to Grain

The first stage of the growing process involves inoculating grain medium with spore solution, and then storing the grain for a period of time to allow mycelium to colonize. Prior to inoculation the grain is soaked, to force it to absorb water, and then loaded into canning jars or spawn bags for sterilization in a pressure cooker. Following inoculation spores will germinate and grow on the grain, forming a network of white mycelium. Mycelium growing on the grain medium is referred to as *grain spawn* or simply *spawn*. The grain should be fully colonized after about two to three weeks, at which point it is ready to be used in the next stage of the growing process.

3.1 GUIDE: PREPARING A SPORE SYRINGE

A spore syringe is used to deliver spore solution (i.e., spores suspended in sterilized water) to the grain medium. A single dark spore print with a 4 cm (1.6 in) diameter will contain enough spores to make up to ten spore syringes. A spore syringe is usually made to contain around 20–25 mL of solution. A single grain jar requires 2–3 mL of spore solution for inoculation, whereas a grain bag requires around 5 mL of solution.

Materials
- Spore print
- Sterilized water
- A metal scraping implement (e.g., scalpel, inoculation loop, metal teaspoon, or something similar)
- Plastic syringe(s)
- A medium-sized jar

Method (see Figure 3.1)

1. Sterilize equipment and materials in the pressure cooker. Fill a jar with the required volume of water (estimate the volume according to the number of spore syringes you intend to make), and then tightly wrap the top of the jar with foil. Don't fit a lid on the jar. Wrap the syringes and metal scraping implement loosely in foil (Figure 3.1A).

   Add water to the pressure cooker per the operation instructions for your cooker. Place three or four jar-lid rings in the base of the pressure cooker (Figure 3.1B), and place the canning rack on top. This raises the equipment out of the water. Load the jar of water and foil package containing the other equipment into the pressure cooker (Figure 3.1C), then cook at 15 psi for thirty minutes.

2. Prepare the sterile work area as described in chapter 2.

3. Transfer sterilized equipment and materials from the pressure cooker to the SAB. Also, place your spore print inside the SAB (Figure 3.1F).

4. Inside the SAB unwrap the foil package containing the syringes, and uncover the jar of sterilized water.

   Unfold the spore print, and then use the teaspoon to scrape spores from the print into the jar (Figure 3.1G). Refold the spore print and set it to one side. Give the jar a swirl to distribute the spores.

5. Fill the first syringe by dipping the needle into the spore solution and then drawing out the plunger. Squirt the contents back into the jar. This ensures the solution is mixed thoroughly (Figure 3.1H).

   Fill each syringe to the desired volume, then fit the caps and rewrap them in foil.

   For best results, wait twelve hours before using the spore syringe. This will allow the spores to become hydrated, and will provide a greater rate of spore germination.

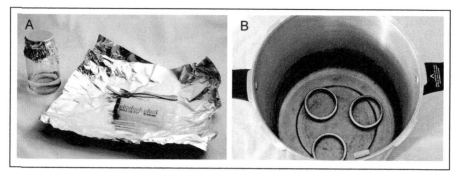

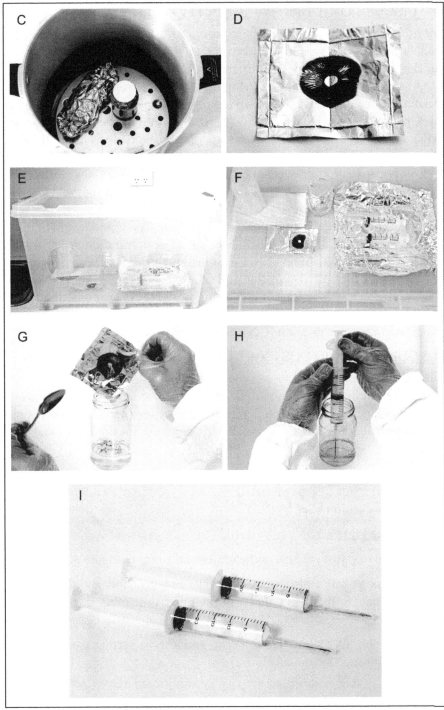

Figure 3.1. Preparing a spore syringe

3.2 DISCUSSION: GRAIN JARS—JAR LID CUSTOMIZATION

Jar lids used for canning must be customized to allow inoculation, and to facilitate gas exchange (GE) between the interior of the jar and the outside air. Fresh oxygen must be able to enter the jar, and excess carbon dioxide (CO_2) produced by growing mycelium must be able to dissipate. If oxygen becomes depleted, or CO_2 builds up too high, mycelial growth will stall or, at best, progress slowly. Filter material must, therefore, be permeable to gases while acting as a barrier to contaminants (see page 65 for a more detailed discussion of GE).

Compressed felt is a perfect filter material. It is reusable, inexpensive, and easily obtainable from craft and fabric stores. Synthetic cushion filler is also perfect for the same reasons.

Other commonly used filter materials include Tyvek and synthetic filter discs (SFDs).Three different methods of jar lid customization are provided. The first guide demonstrates the simplest method possible, where a single port acts as the site for both inoculation and GE. A second, more polished, option shows how to install self-healing injection ports, thus separating the site of inoculation from the GE vent. The last method is suitable for jars that will be inoculated via grain-to-grain (G2G) transfers (see page 124).

3.3 GUIDE: JAR LID CUSTOMIZATION—SYNTHETIC CUSHION FILLER

This guide outlines a simple-but-effective means for customizing jar lids by using synthetic cushion filler (often referred to as Poly-Fil, a common brand of synthetic filler). A single port is made to act as both the point of inoculation and GE.

Materials
- Canning jar lids (plastic or metal)
- Synthetic cushion filler

Method (see Figure 3.3)

1. Drill a 10 mm (0.4 in) hole in the center of the jar lid (Figure 3.3A).

2. Compress, or roll, a piece of cushion filler in your hand, and then press it into the hole in the jar lid. Pull it through from the other side, ensuring a tight fit.

The cushion filler allows GE to occur, and a spore syringe can be pushed straight through for inoculation.

Figure 3.3. Jar lid customization–synthetic cushion filler

3.4 GUIDE: JAR LID CUSTOMIZATION–SELF-HEALING INJECTION PORTS

This guide describes how to make lids that have separate sites for inoculation and GE. Inoculation is carried out by inserting a syringe needle through the rubber injection port, which seals as the syringe is removed. GE occurs through a separate filtered vent.

Materials
- Canning jar lids (plastic or metal)
- Self-healing injection ports
- Compressed felt
- RTV silicone

Method (see Figure 3.4)

1. Cut one disk (3 cm diameter) of compressed felt per lid (Figure 3.4A).

2. Drill holes in your jar lid, positioned opposite as shown (Figure 3.4B). One hole should be about 10 mm (0.4 in) in diameter, whereas the second hole should be just large enough to provide a snug fit for the injection port.

3. Apply silicone to the underside edge of one of the rubber injection ports (Figure 3.4C), and then press it firmly into the smaller hole in the jar lid (Figure 3.4D). Note that injection ports and felt disks can be fixed to the bench with Blu-tack to stop them from sliding around while silicone is applied.

4. Take a disk of compressed felt and, on one side, run a bead of silicone around the edge (Figure 3.4E). Place it directly over the second hole in the lid. Press down firmly to ensure good contact (Figure 3.4F). Allow the silicone to set for twenty-four to thirty-six hours before use.

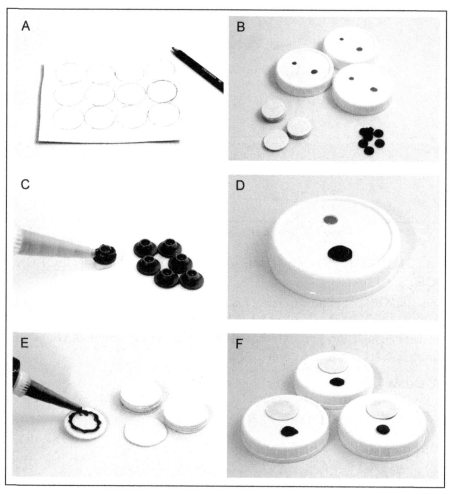

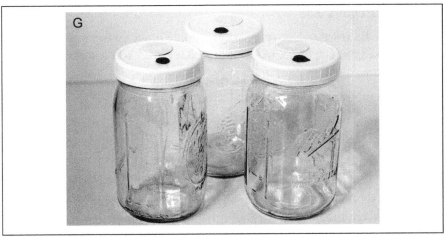

Figure 3.4. Jar lid customization—self-healing injection ports

It is possible to make a rudimentary injection port by entirely filling one of the holes with heat-resistant silicone (as shown in the image below). The silicone itself can act as a self-healing injection port.

This lid has a self-healing injection port made from RTV silicone.

3.5 GUIDE: JAR LID CUSTOMIZATION—COMPRESSED FELT DISKS

Jar lids customized with the following method aren't designed to facilitate inoculation with a spore syringe. Lids customized this way should be used only on jars that will be inoculated via G2G transfer.

Materials
- Canning jar lids (plastic or metal)
- Compressed felt

Method (see Figure 3.5)

1. Using the lid from one of your jars as a guide, trace circles onto a sheet of compressed felt (Figure 3.5A). Cut out each circle. You will need one disk of compressed felt for each grain jar.

2. Drill several small holes in each lid to act as vents for GE (Figure 3.5B).

3. If using metal lids, place the lid on top of the jar first, followed by a disk of compressed felt, and then screw down the lid ring. If using plastic lids, place the felt on top of the jar first, and then screw down the lid on top. The felt should fit the mouth of the jar perfectly with no gaps showing.

Tyvek or synthetic filter discs can be used in place of compressed felt. If using Tyvek, cut the filters to be larger than the neck of the jar, and allow the material to hang down the sides a little way.

Figure 3.5. Jar lid customization–compressed felt disks

3.6 DISCUSSION: GRAIN MEDIUM (WILD BIRDSEED)

Wild birdseed (WBS) makes a perfect substrate for mushroom mycelium once it has been hydrated and sterilized. WBS is inexpensive and easily obtainable from pet-supply stores. It will be soaked and heated, causing it to soften and absorb water. It will then be loaded into jars or bags and sterilized in the pressure cooker. Once cooled, the WBS can be inoculated with spore solution.

WBS typically contains a combination of grains, such as wheat, sorghum, corn, oats, millet, and sunflower. Some growers prefer to remove specific grains (e.g., sunflower seeds and corn kernels) because they believe these types of grains can become more easily contaminated, or, as is the case with corn, become sticky. In reality, removing specific seed types isn't necessary, and doing so depends on personal preference. Mycelium will colonize on all seed types typically found in commercial WBS.

20 kg bag of WBS

When measuring out grain for soaking, remember that WBS will expand as it absorbs water. As a rule of thumb, seven, full-quart jars of dry grain will give roughly ten quarts of hydrated grain, although this will vary depending on the exact composition of grains in your chosen WBS mix.

Another thing to remember when loading grain jars is that space should always be left in the top of each jar. This is because partially colonized grain needs to be shaken to distribute mycelium evenly throughout the jar, and leaving space in the top makes it easier to ensure this happens. Jars that will be inoculated with spore solution should be filled to three-fourths capacity, whereas jars destined for G2G transfers should be two-thirds filled to allow space for the addition of colonized grain at a later date.

The following steps can be used to estimate the required volume of dry grain when preparing our grain medium:

1. First, determine the total amount of hydrated grain needed. In this example, we want 12 jars, three-fourths of the way full, which is equal to nine full quarts.

   $$= (12 / 100\%) \times 75\% = 9 \text{ qt}$$

2. Now, multiply this value by 70 percent to estimate the required volume of dry grain.

   $$= (9 \text{ qt} / 100\%) \times 70\% = 6.3 \text{ qt}$$

   A quantity of 6.3 quarts of dry grain will give us 9 quarts of hydrated grain.

3.7 GUIDE: GRAIN MEDIUM—SOAKING GRAIN AND LOADING JARS

WBS is rinsed to remove dust, and then soaked, causing it to absorb water. The hydrated grain is then loaded into canning jars for sterilization in a pressure cooker.

Materials
- Canning jars and lids
- A large heavy-based cooking pot (the base of the pressure cooker can be used)
- WBS
- Large wire-mesh strainer
- Gypsum (optional)
- Freshly brewed coffee (optional)

Method (see Figure 3.7)

1. Use a quart jar to scoop the desired volume of dry WBS into the cooking pot (Figure 3.7A).

2. Fill the cooking pot with tap water until it covers the WBS by about 5 cm (2 in), then rinse the grain to remove dust and unwanted debris. Use your hand or a wooden spoon to swirl water through the grain. Pour the water off. Repeat this process. Rinse the grain two to three times, or until the water appears much cleaner when poured off.

   It's up to you whether you retain floating seeds or throw them away. In this example, floating sunflower seeds are collected in a strainer after each rinse (Figure 3.7B), and then returned to the rest of the grain.

3. After rinsing the grain, fill the pot with water until it covers the WBS by 5 cm (2 in), and leave it to soak for 12 hours. As it soaks, the grain will expand. Add additional water as necessary to ensure the grain remains completely covered.

Optional: Add gypsum (Figure 3.7D) and freshly brewed coffee (Figure 3.7E) to the soaking grain at a ratio of 1 tablespoon gypsum to 3 quarts dried grain and/or 2 cups coffee to 3 quarts dried grain (add the liquid coffee, discard the coffee grounds). Including one or both of these ingredients will add beneficial nutrients to the grain to aid mycelial growth; however, neither is essential.

4. After soaking the grain for 12 hours, place the cooking pot on a stove top and bring it to the brink of boiling (Figure 3.7F). Stir often to prevent the grain from sticking, and to ensure even distribution of heat throughout the pot.

Heating the grain will soften it and maximize water absorption. Boiling can result in burst grains, so turn the heat off before boiling can occur. Allow the grain to sit and cool for 30 minutes.

5. Strain the grain through a mesh strainer (Figure 3.7G) and allow the water to run down the sink. Shake the strainer vigorously to remove as much excess water as possible. If you are preparing a large volume of grain, you'll need to do this in batches.

6. Load the hydrated grain into canning jars (Figure 3.7H), leaving space in the top of each jar.

7. Fit the lids, then wrap aluminum foil over the top of each jar (Figure 3.7J).

NOTE: If you see water pooling excessively in the bottom of the jars, then the grain was too wet when the jars were loaded.

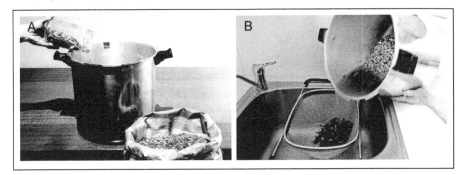

Figure 3.7. Grain medium—soaking grain and loading jars

3.8 GUIDE: GRAIN MEDIUM—PRESSURE-COOKER STERILIZATION

Grain medium must be properly sterilized prior to inoculation to kill off any unwanted microbes that could otherwise contaminate the grain and interfere with our mushroom mycelium.

Materials
- Jars containing prepared WBS medium
- Pressure cooker

Method (see Figure 3.8)

1. Place the canning rack into the pressure cooker, and add the appropriate amount of water (Figure 3.8A). Next, load the grain jars, and cook them at 15 psi (Figure 3.8E) for 120 minutes. It's perfectly fine to lay one or two jars on their sides on top of the first layer of jars (Figure 3.8C). The foil covers prevent water from entering the jars and interfering with the water content of the grain medium.

2. Allow the jars to cool inside the pressure cooker for 1.5–2 hours. Transfer jars straight from the pressure cooker to the SAB to carry out inoculation. Alternatively, sterilized jars can be temporarily stored in a clean plastic tub with the lid fitted until they are needed for inoculation.

Figure 3.8. Grain medium—pressure-cooker sterilization

3.9 GUIDE: GRAIN MEDIUM—SPORE-SYRINGE INOCULATION

Sterilized WBS is now ready to be inoculated with spore solution.

Materials
- Spore syringes
- Sterilized grain jars

Method (see Figure 3.9)

1. Prepare the sterile work area as described in chapter 2.

2. Place spore syringes inside the SAB and transfer sterilized grain jars from the pressure cooker directly to the SAB (Figure 3.9A).

3. Inside the SAB, remove the foil from the top of each jar.

4. Pick up a spore syringe, and give it a vigorous tap to disperse spores evenly throughout the solution (Figure 3.9C).

5. Uncap the syringe, and then bring the syringe outside the SAB to flame sterilize the needle (Figure 3.9D). Heat the needle from the tip to a point two-thirds of its length. Hold the needle in the flame for three to five seconds until it glows red. Next, bring the spore syringe back inside the SAB.

   Your movements should be unhurried and methodical. Avoid making rushed, abrupt movements that could generate air currents. Don't use your fingers to touch the syringe needle or the inoculation point on the jar.

6. While holding the syringe in one hand, use your free hand to grip a grain jar. Push the needle into the injection port (Figure 3.9E). Don't insert the needle beyond the point that was sterilized. Squeeze 2–3 mL of spore solution into the jar.

   Aim the spore solution so that it lands in one spot. The chance of mycelium forming is improved by allowing the spores to settle close together on the grain.

7. Remove the needle, and set the jar to the opposite side of the SAB so you won't lose track of which jars have been inoculated. Repeat the process for each jar, remembering to flame the needle between each inoculation. Label the jars with the date of inoculation and appropriate identifying information (Figure 3.9F).

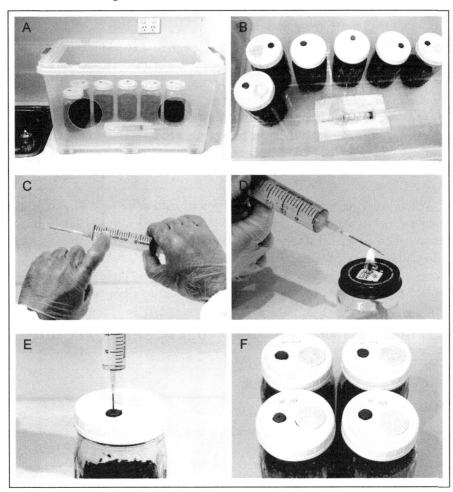

Figure 3.9. Grain medium—spore-syringe inoculation

3.10 DISCUSSION: SPAWN BAGS AS AN ALTERNATIVE TO JARS

Spawn bags can be used as an alternative to canning jars for holding grain medium. Spawn bags hold larger volumes of grain than jars, and make it possible to sterilize more grain per pressure-cooking cycle. A single bag can (optimally) hold 3–5 L (3.2–5.4 qt) of hydrated grain.

Spawn bags come with filter patches that are normally rated at 0.2 or 0.5 micrometers (μm), a reference to the size of the pores in the filter. Both ratings will reliably prevent contaminants from entering the bag; however, 0.5 μm is recommended because the larger pores allow greater GE.

It is possible to reuse bags two to three times, but they are nowhere near as robust as jars, and will weaken after only a few cycles through the pressure cooker. Spawn bags are usually discarded after a single use.

Spawn bags may come with built-in, self-healing injection ports to facilitate inoculation with spore solution, but not always. Bags that don't come with injection ports can be inoculated straight through the bag with a spore syringe.

Working with spawn bags does present a few challenges. Larger volumes of grain take longer to colonize, and are, therefore, at greater risk of contamination, because any heat-resistant bacterial spores (*endospores*) that survived sterilization have a longer window of opportunity to germinate. For this reason, spawn bags should be filled with a manageable amount of grain that will fully colonize in as little time as possible. Contamination of a spawn bag represents a greater loss of materials than contamination of a single quart jar.

When working with spawn bags, you should also be aware of their vulnerability to bursting during sterilization in the pressure cooker. This can occur when air inside the bag expands as it warms. If the heated air can't adequately escape, the bag will burst. To avoid this situation, you should leave spawn bags unsealed during sterilization and load them into the cooker in such a way that the filter patch is unobstructed to allow venting to occur through the filter.

3.11 GUIDE: SPAWN BAGS—PREPARATION, STERILIZATION, AND INOCULATION

Filling and Sterilizing Spawn Bags

Materials
- Hydrated WBS
- Spawn bags
- Ziploc ties

Method (see Figure 3.11.1)

1. Fill spawn bags with hydrated WBS (Figure 3.11.1A). It isn't recommended to fill bags with more than 5 L (5.4 qt) of hydrated grain. Follow the procedure outlined on page 22 to wash and hydrate your grain.

2. Don't seal the bags before pressure cooking. Fold the flap, expelling excess air in the process (Figure 3.11.1C). Ensure the filter patch is pointing outward as shown (Figure 3.11.1E). Air will breathe through the filter patch and neck of the bags, thus preventing the bags from bursting.

3. Place four jar-lid rings in the base of the pressure cooker, followed by the canning rack. Load the spawn bags as shown. Use lid rings as spacers between the bags and sides of the pressure cooker (Figure 3.11.1H). This is to ensure consistent airflow between the bags.

If your pressure cooker is big enough, you should be able to layer the bags as shown (Figure 3.11.1I). Place an additional canning rack or more lid rings between the top and bottom layers.

The topmost bags should be weighted down with a ceramic plate or similarly heavy object (Figure 3.11.1J) to prevent the bag flaps from flailing about and possibly covering the vent hole of the pressure cooker.

4. Follow the pressure-cooker operating procedures. Be sure to add the appropriate volume of water to the pressure cooker. Maintain 15 psi for 120 minutes. Allow sterilized bags to cool for a minimum of two hours before removing them from the pressure cooker.

5. Spawn bags can be sealed straight away with Ziploc ties (Figure 3.11.1K) or inoculated via G2G transfer first.

After sealing the bags, allow them to inflate by drawing air through the filter. Colonizing mycelium needs oxygen to grow, so it's a good idea to make sure the top portion of the bags are expanded with air.

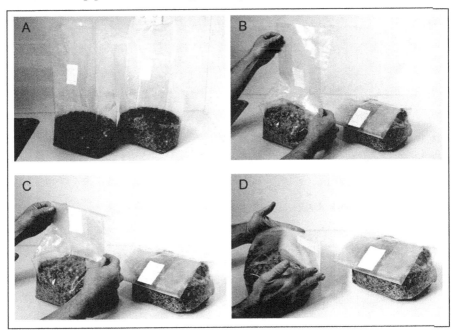

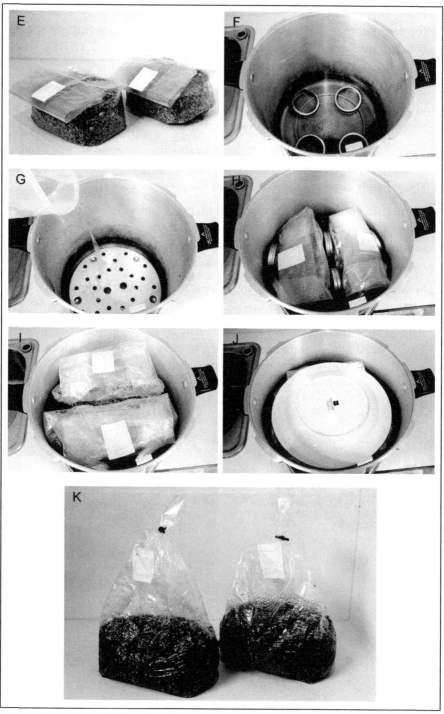

Figure 3.11.1. Filling and sterilizing spawn bags

Inoculating Spawn Bags

This method describes inoculating with a spore syringe. For details about G2G transfers, see page 124. Inoculation should be performed inside a SAB. This can be challenging because it is usually possible to fit only one or two bags at a time. Be sure never to use your fingers to touch the filter patch or point of inoculation.

Materials

- Spore syringe(s)
- Sterilized bags of grain
- 3M Micropore tape (optional)

Method (see Figure 3.11.2)

1. Prepare the sterile work area as described in chapter 2, and transfer materials into the SAB.

2. Flame-sterilize the syringe needle. Allow it to cool for 30 seconds.

3. Push the tip of the needle directly through the bag, or through the self-healing injection port, if present. If inoculating through the bag use a pen to mark beside the point of inoculation. This will allow you to easily find and cover the hole following inoculation (Figure 3.11.2B).

   Don't push the needle beyond the point that was flame-sterilized. Squirt 2.5 mL of spore solution onto the grain to one side of the point of inoculation (Figure 3.11.2C). Without removing the needle, squirt another 2.5 mL to the other side of the point of inoculation (Figure 3.11.2D). By pooling spore solution at two different points, we hope to speed the rate of colonization.

4. If inoculating directly through the bag, promptly cover the point of inoculation with a layer of 3M Micropore tape (Figure 3.11.2E).

5. Repeat these steps for each bag, and remember to flame-sterilize the needle between each inoculation. Label the bags with the date of inoculation and appropriate identifying information.

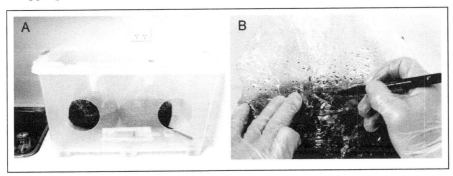

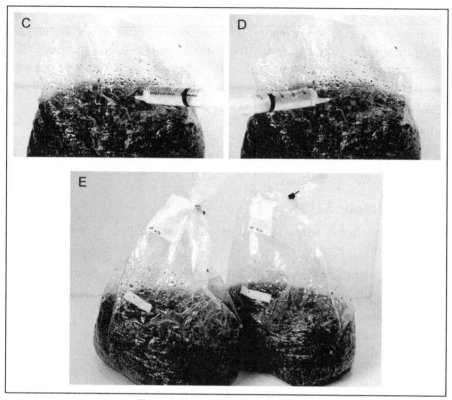

Figure 3.11.2. Inoculating spawn bags

3.12 DISCUSSION: STORING INOCULATED GRAIN

Store inoculated grain out of direct sunlight on a shelf or in a cupboard. Grain spawn will grow equally well in the dark or when exposed to typical household lighting. A plastic tub makes a convenient storage compartment, provided the lid is fit loosely to allow sufficient GE.

A plastic tub makes a convenient storage compartment for colonizing grain.

Grain stored on a shelf in a wardrobe

Within four to eight days, small points of white mycelial growth should appear on the grain, and begin to radiate outward. Roughly one to two weeks after the first signs of growth, you should shake or break up the grain to redistribute the mycelium throughout the jar or bag. Doing this will ensure even colonization of the grain, and speed up the total colonization time. Jars may need to be shaken only once, whereas spawn bags may need to be broken up twice to ensure even colonization.

Jars can be shaken by tapping the side against something firm but with a little give (e.g., a foam exercise roller, a phone book, or the padded arm of a couch) (Figure 3.12.1B). Grain in spawn bags can be broken up with your fingers on the outside of the bag (Figure 3.12.1D). Try to prevent grain from contacting the filter patch.

Note that shaking the grain can bruise the mycelium and cause it to stain blue. The blueing effect is a result of oxidization, and is a characteristic trait of *P. cubensis* and other psilocin-containing mushrooms. Blueing is no cause for concern, for bruised mycelium will quickly recover and continue to grow.

Grain can be considered completely colonized when white mycelium covers all portions of the grain medium. At that stage, the grain spawn is ready to be mixed with bulk substrate to undergo another period of colonization, followed by fruiting.

Figure 3.12.1. Breaking up colonizing grain

Fully colonized grain jars

Healthy grain spawn

Fully colonized spawn bags

A Few Words on Temperature

In general terms, mycelial growth proceeds slowly at colder temperatures, and speeds up as the temperature increases. The optimal temperature range for grain spawn incubation is about 24–26°C (75–79°F). Grain jars stored in this temperature range should colonize fully within ten to twenty days. Spawn bags may take a few days longer because they contain a larger volume of grain. By comparison, grain spawn stored below 15°C (59°F) may take up to four weeks or longer to colonize completely.

Temperatures above 27°C (80°F) may be favorable for certain types of bacteria. Therefore, increasing the temperature above 27°C (80°F) can increase the chance of contamination by providing optimal growing conditions for microbial endospores that survived sterilization. Thus, it is better to keep spawn incubation temperatures below 27°C (80°F).

Usually, no special steps are required to manage the temperature of incubating grain spawn. Ambient household temperatures are normally close to the optimal range. In situations where very cold ambient conditions are the norm, an incubation chamber may be useful. A simple-but-effective incubation chamber can be made by sitting a tub over a seedling-propagation mat. The tub should be raised on spacers to create a gap between the base of the tub and the propagation mat (Figure 3.12.2B). This arrangement allows excess heat to dissipate and prevents the base of the tub from heating up excessively.

In the images below, the ambient temperature is 16.1°C (61°F), whereas the temperature inside the tub is considerably warmer at 23.5°C (74.3°F) (Figure 3.12.2C).

Be aware that growing mycelium produces its own heat, and the internal temperature of colonizing grain spawn can be higher than ambient temperatures. This is especially true for spawn bags, which hold a greater volume of mycelium than jars. Keep this in mind when considering storage temperatures.

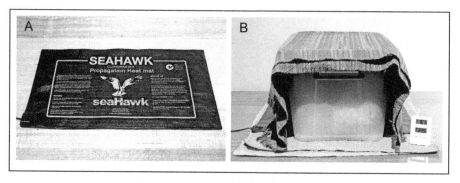

Figure 3.12.2. Storing grain—temperature

3.13 DISCUSSION: CONTAMINATION ON GRAIN

In the days after inoculation, pay close attention to your grain to identify any mold or bacterial contaminants. Contamination can take the form of anything other than pearly white mycelium. Mold will often be brightly colored, and may be green, pink, orange, or black patches of growth. In addition, some mold is white, and can be difficult to differentiate from the mushroom mycelium. Mold may grow directly on previously healthy mycelium.

Bacterial contamination will often cause the grain to look slimy. You may notice an increased amount of condensation between the grain and around the neck of the jar. Usually, mushroom mycelium won't colonize areas of grain that contain bacterial contamination, so bacteria may be revealed as sections of grain that remain un-colonized.

Smell is a very important indicator of contamination. Healthy, uncontaminated mycelium should give off a pleasant, distinctive, "mushroomy" scent. Any other kind of smell can indicate contamination. Odors that could be described as sour, fermented, sickly, sweet, or rotten indicate contamination. When mixing grain spawn with bulk substrate or using it in G2G transfers, you should always smell the grain immediately after removing the lid, and before taking any further steps.

Contaminated grain must be identified as soon as possible and separated from healthy grain. There is no way to save contaminated grain. Under no circumstances should a contaminated jar be opened inside or anywhere near the healthy grain spawn. Empty the jar or bag outside.

Expect to get the occasional contaminated jar, especially in the early stages while perfecting your aseptic technique. One or two contaminated jars in a batch of 12, for example, could be considered acceptable for a beginner grower. With practice and experience, you will reduce your rate of contamination to zero.

Mold growing on grain

Excessive condensation around the neck of a severely contaminated grain jar

CHAPTER 4

From Grain to Bulk Substrate

This chapter will discuss *spawning to bulk*, the process of using grain spawn to inoculate a mixture of bulk substrate. Grain spawn is combined with bulk substrate mixture and left to completely colonize before being induced to produce fruit. The remainder of the growth will occur inside the fruiting chamber.

Spawning to bulk is performed in open-air conditions. From this point, we are no longer required to maintain a completely sterile environment for the mycelium to grow in. The aim now is to provide the growing mycelium with optimal growing conditions so it has the best-possible chance to completely colonize the bulk substrate. It is usually possible to harvest multiple flushes of fruit from a single bulk substrate.

4.1 DISCUSSION: THE FRUITING CHAMBER

A fruiting chamber is a terrarium-like structure used to create conditions favorable for mycelial growth and fruiting. It allows us to regulate movement of air and gases, humidity, and entry of light. By manipulating these environmental conditions, we are able to create an environment suitable for vegetative growth and then switch to conditions that will encourage fruiting.

In this chapter, we'll focus on setting up the fruiting chamber for a period of vegetative colonization. Fruiting conditions and the process of fruiting a bulk substrate are discussed in detail in chapter 5.

Monotub — An Overview

The *monotub* is an extremely effective fruiting chamber for bulk growing. Other styles of fruiting chambers exist; however, monotubs are recommended because they are easy to make, require very little maintenance, provide high yields, and allow for the grow operation to be easily scaled up. The monotub is designed to allow internal humidity and gas levels to remain optimal with only minor adjustments required over the duraction of the grow.

The monotub is made from a large, transparent, plastic tub with a transparent lid. A tub that holds 50–70 L (53–74 qt) is a good size, allowing ample space for a high-yielding crop while remaining light enough to be easily handled. Smaller-volume monotubs are often referred to as *mini-monotubs*.

The tub should be stackable to allow easy storage of multiple monotubs. Holes are positioned in the sides of the tub to facilitate the movement of gases and air. These are referred to as fresh-air exchange (FAE) holes (see page 65 for a detailed explanation of FAE).

4.2 GUIDE: CONSTRUCTING A MONOTUB FRUITING CHAMBER

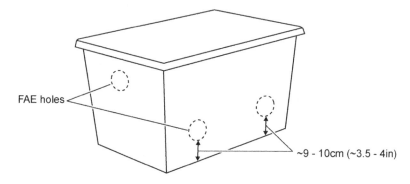

Materials

- Large plastic tub
- Drill with about a 5 cm (2 in) hole cutter
- Marker pen

Method (see Figure 4.2)

1. Mark the hole positions on the sides of the tub. The monotub will have six FAE holes drilled into its sides. The long sides will have two holes positioned almost level with the top of the bulk substrate. The base of each hole should be 9–10 cm (3.5–4 in) from the bottom of the tub. The short sides will each have a single hole centered and positioned as high and close to the lid as shown.

2. Use the drill plus the attachment to cut the holes in the sides of the plastic tub (Figure 4.2A). The monotub is now complete and ready for use (Figure 4.2B).

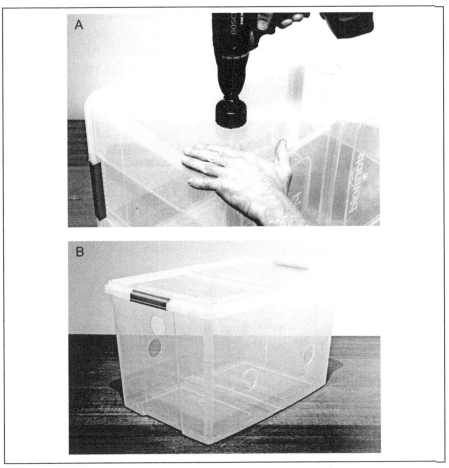

Figure 4.2. Constructing a monotub fruiting chamber

4.3 DISCUSSION: GROWING WITH BULK SUBSTRATE

In the next stage of the growing operation, we take colonized grain spawn and combine it with bulk substrate, a process referred to as spawning to bulk. The mycelium undergoes a further period of growth as it colonizes the bulk substrate. In this way, the total amount of mycelium is increased, allowing for a higher (bulk) yield of mushrooms.

From this point on, there is no requirement to keep the growing conditions sterile. Spawning to bulk is performed in the open air, not in our clean work area. The aim now is to provide optimal growing conditions to the mycelium in order to give it the best-possible chance to colonize and dominate the bulk substrate. Once fully colonized, the bulk substrate will remain fairly resistant to contamination for a period long enough to harvest several flushes of mushrooms. Inevitably, the bulk substrate will eventually become contaminated, but we hope to achieve two to three flushes before this happens.

Complete colonization of the bulk substrate can take anywhere from two weeks to a month or more from the time of inoculation with grain spawn. The rate of colonization is influenced by substrate depth, the ratio of spawn to bulk substrate mixture, bulk substrate ingredients, and conditions inside the chamber.

Bulk Substrate Ingredients

Ingredients used in bulk substrate are chosen for their nutritional value, suitability as a substrate and/or water-retention qualities, and include materials such as manure, coffee grounds, straw, coconut fiber (coir), compost/worm castings, vermiculite, and gypsum. An effective bulk substrate can be prepared using different combinations of these materials. Ensure that the bulk substrate includes a source of nutrition for the growing mycelium, plus the ability to absorb and retain water.

Manure

Manure is a fairly obvious choice of ingredient because *P. cubensis* is commonly found growing on dung in a natural setting. The best bulk substrate recipes include some form of manure. Manure is an excellent source of nutrition, and will help to create great yields. It should be dried, not fresh, and should be thoroughly crumbled before use. Dried horse or cow manure is ideal. Chicken manure can also be used, but note that it is much richer, and should be used in smaller quantities relative to other ingredients.

Compost and worm castings/vermicompost

Composted food and organic matter that worms have broken down is referred to as *worm castings* or *vermicompost*, and is basically worm manure. Vermicompost can be used as a source of nutrition in bulk substrate. It should be well degraded, smell like soil, and have a crumbly consistency.

Spent coffee grounds

Spent coffee grounds are a common bulk substrate ingredient. Coffee grounds contain nutrients that ensure healthy mycelial growth. Grounds can be used in combination with manure or on their own. Growers who don't have easy access to manure can produce nice yields using coffee grounds combined with coconut fiber and vermiculite.

Coffee grounds can be prone to contamination; therefore, brew them immediately before use. Don't use spent coffee grounds that have been collected over days or weeks because storing damp coffee grounds before use allows them to collect mold and bacteria. Also, don't use un-brewed coffee straight from the packet.

Spent coffee grounds should be used sparingly because adding too much can make the substrate too rich. It is recommended that coffee grounds should not exceed 5 percent of the total bulk substrate volume.

Coconut fiber (coir)

Coconut fiber, also known as *coir*, is a fibrous material derived from the husks of coconuts. It has excellent water-retention properties, making it perfect for maintaining high water content in bulk substrate, while simultaneously keeping the substrate aerated. Although coconut fiber may provide a small amount of nutrition to bulk substrate, its main benefit is its water-absorbing capacity and suitability as a substrate for mycelium to grow in. Coconut fiber should, therefore, be combined with other sources of nutrition.

Coconut fiber is typically purchased as compressed bricks. It is important to avoid any coconut fiber products that have slow-release fertilizer or fungicides added to them. Coir bricks can be cut into portions with a handsaw and added to the bulk substrate mixture in its compressed form; it will expand when water is added. Alternatively, a brick of coconut fiber can be hydrated and crumbled ahead of time and measured out in its uncompressed form. One brick usually yields 8–9 L (8.5–9.5 qt) of uncompressed coconut fiber.

Vermiculite

Vermiculite is another excellent material for maximizing the water absorbency and aeration of bulk substrate. Vermiculite is a nonorganic silicate mineral. Similar to coir, it provides only a small amount of nutritional value, and should, therefore, be used in combination with other nutrient sources.

Gypsum (calcium sulfate, CaSO4 2H2O)

Gypsum is a mineral commonly used as a fertilizer and soil conditioner. Used as an ingredient in bulk substrate, it serves as a source of nutrition and will help ensure excellent yields, providing calcium and sulfur to growing mycelium. Gypsum is not considered to add volume to the bulk substrate mixture. It is added at a rate of 1 percent of the total bulk substrate volume.

Straw

Straw provides an excellent substrate for mycelium. It should be thoroughly mulched before being mixed with other bulk substrate ingredients. Use garden shears to cut clumps of straw into small pieces.

Water

Like all living things, mushrooms are made up of mostly water. Water is added to the bulk substrate mixture in a quantity that will achieve field capacity (see page 55). As a rule of thumb, 0.4 L of water is added for every 1 L of bulk substrate mixture.

Sample Bulk Substrate Recipes

The following examples demonstrate workable and effective bulk substrate recipes. These recipes can be used exactly as described, or they can be varied according to the availability of ingredients or personal preference.

Recipe 1 (Manure—An Excellent All-rounder)

This recipe is easy and effective and produces great yields.

- 40% dried and pulverized horse manure

- 30% coconut fiber

- 30% vermiculite

- 0.4 L water for every 1 L of bulk substrate mixture

Recipe 2 (Coffee Grounds—A Minimalist Recipe)

This recipe might be useful for people living in a city or who otherwise have limited access to agricultural supplies.

- 95% coconut fiber

- 5% spent coffee grounds

- 0.4 L water for every 1 L of bulk substrate mixture

Recipe 3 (Coir, Vermiculite, and Gypsum—Another Minimalist Alternative)

Gypsum provides the nutrition in this recipe.

- 50% coconut fiber

- 50% vermiculite

- 1% gypsum

- 0.4 L water for every 1 L of bulk substrate mixture

Recipe 4 (Complete—Turbocharged)

If access to materials is no obstacle, then go all out.

- 35% dried and pulverized horse manure

- 30% coconut fiber

- 30% vermiculite

- 5% spent coffee grounds

- 1% gypsum

- 0.4 L water for every 1 L of bulk substrate mixture

4.4 GUIDE: BULK SUBSTRATE—CALCULATING VOLUMES

Calculating the relative volume of each ingredient is an essential preliminary step to bulk substrate preparation. Two examples are provided here to demonstrate how this is achieved.

Example 1 uses recipe 1 from above ("Manure—An Excellent All-arounder), and example 2 uses recipe 4 ("Complete—Turbocharged). The calculations shown can be adjusted according to monotub dimensions, ratio of ingredients, and ratio of spawn to bulk substrate.

Fully colonized grain is mixed with the bulk substrate at a ratio close to 1:1, 2:3, or similar (e.g., 1:1 = 50% grain spawn + 50% bulk substrate mixture, 2:3 = 40% grain spawn + 60% bulk substrate mixture). The more grain spawn that is included, the faster the bulk substrate will colonize. It isn't recommended to use less than 30 percent grain spawn when spawning to bulk. Using insufficient grain spawn will result in slow colonization, and this can lead to an increased risk of contamination before the mycelium is able to completely colonize and dominate the bulk substrate.

The depth of the grain spawn, plus bulk substrate mixture, should be between 6–10 cm (2.5–4 in). Substrates thicker than this can take too long to colonize, and may become prone to contamination. On the other hand, if the substrate is too thin, total yield tends to be lower than it could have been.

Example 1. Manure—An Excellent All-rounder
50% grain spawn + 50% bulk substrate mixture (1:1)

Bulk substrate ingredients
40% dried and pulverized horse manure
30% coconut fiber (coir)
30% vermiculite
0.4 L water for every 1 L of bulk substrate mixture

Multiply the width and length of the tub by the intended depth of the substrate. This will tell us the total volume of spawn plus bulk substrate required.

The diagram below shows a typical 50 L (53 qt) monotub with dimensions 50 cm long × 30 cm wide (20 × 12 in). In addition, we know that the optimum depth for a bulk substrate is 6–10 cm (2.5–4 in). In this example, we'll make our bulk substrate 8 cm (3 in) deep. We can therefore calculate the total volume of grain spawn plus bulk substrate to be held in the tub:

50 cm × 30 cm × 8 cm = 12,000 cm3 (=12,000 mL)
12,000 mL = 12 L (12.7 qt)

Note that 50 percent of this volume (6,000 mL) will be taken up by spawn from our colonized grain jars. The remaining volume (6,000 mL) will be made up of bulk substrate ingredients, which we'll mix in the following ratio: horse manure (40%), coconut fiber (30%), and vermiculite (30%).

Knowing we need a total of 6,000 mL of bulk substrate, we can calculate the amount of each ingredient required:

Horse manure = (6,000 mL / 100) × 40% = 2,400 mL (=2.4 L or 2.5 qt)
Coconut fiber = (6,000 mL / 100) × 30% = 1,800 mL (=1.8 L or 1.9 qt)
Vermiculite = (6,000 mL / 100) × 30% = 1,800 mL (=1.8 L or 1.9 qt)
Water = 6 L × 0.4 L = 2.4 L (2.5 qt)

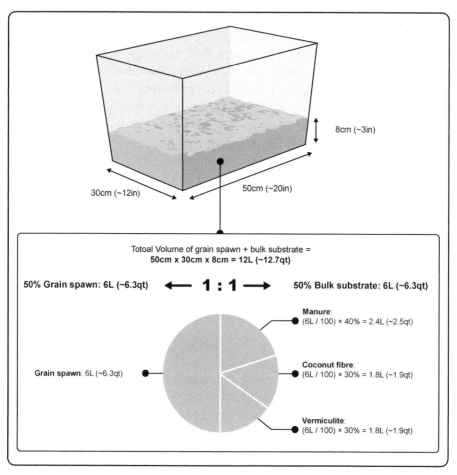

Figure 4.4.1. Example 1. manure—an excellent all-rounder

Example 2. Complete—Turbocharged
40% grain spawn + 60% bulk substrate mixture (2:3)

Bulk substrate ingredients
35% dried and pulverized horse manure
30% coconut fiber (coir)
30% vermiculite
5% spent coffee grounds
1% gypsum
0.4 L water for every 1 L of bulk substrate mixture

Total volume of grain spawn plus substrate to be held in the tub:

50 cm × 30 cm × 8 cm = 12,000 mL (12 L or 12.7 qt)

Grain spawn = (12,000 mL /100) × 40% = 4,800 mL (4.8 L or 5.1 qt)
Bulk substrate = (12,000 mL / 100) × 60% = 7,200 mL (7.2 L or 7.6 qt)

Knowing we need a total of 7,200 mL of bulk substrate, we can calculate the amount of each ingredient required:

Horse manure = (7,200 mL / 100) × 35% = 2,520 mL (=2.52 L or 2.6 qt)
Coconut fiber = (7,200 mL / 100) × 30% = 2,160 mL (=2.16 L or 2.3 qt)
Vermiculite = (7,200 mL / 100) × 30% = 2,160 mL (=2.16 L or 2.3 qt)
Coffee grounds = (7,200 mL / 100) × 5% = 360 mL (=0.36 L or 0.38 qt)
Gypsum = (7,200 mL / 100) × 1% = 72 mL (= 0.15 pt)
Water = 7.2 L × 0.4 L = 2.9 L (3 qt)

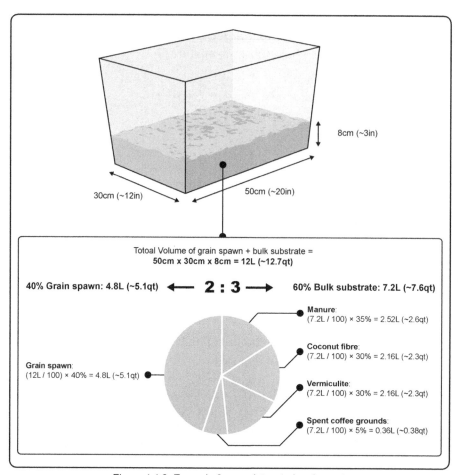

Figure 4.4.2. Example 2. complete—turbo charged

4.5 DISCUSSION: BULK SUBSTRATE—PASTEURIZATION

Pasteurization is a critical step in the preparation of bulk substrate. Pasteurization involves heating a material to around 60–65°C (140–149°F) for a set amount of time, then allowing it to cool. This process differs from sterilization in that it doesn't kill all the microorganisms present; rather, it reduces the microbial load, killing off those microbes susceptible to temperatures of up to 65°C (149°F). The remaining microorganisms aren't detrimental to the growing mycelium, and actually have the beneficial effect of helping prevent problematic microbes from establishing before the mycelium has time to colonize and dominate the substrate. If bulk substrate is completely or partially sterilized, it becomes more susceptible to contamination later on, for problematic microbes can more easily gain a foothold in the absence of any competition. Sterilization of bulk substrate is therefore avoided in favor of pasteurization.

Two methods for bulk substrate pasteurization are discussed. The bucket method uses the application of boiling water directly to the bulk substrate ingredients to hydrate and pasteurize in one step. In most cases, it provides excellent results, and has the added advantage of being extremely easy to execute. This method should be the first option in most cases purely due to ease of use.

A more thorough alternative for pasteurizing on a stove is also provided. This method involves loading hydrated bulk substrate mixture into polypropylene bags or canning jars and heating it in boiling water on a stove. The stove-top method should be employed when working with bulk substrate ingredients that are more susceptible to contamination, such as spent coffee grounds.

4.6 GUIDE: BULK SUBSTRATE PASTEURIZATION—BUCKET METHOD

The key to successful application of the bucket method is ensuring that boiling water can penetrate evenly throughout the ingredients. Particular attention must be given to ensure the manure is broken up very well. Clumps of manure may not be adequately penetrated and pasteurized by the boiling water, and this can result in premature contamination of bulk substrate later on.

Materials
- Painter's bucket with a tight sealing lid (the lid should have a small vent hole)
- Boiling water
- Bulk substrate ingredients

Method (see Figure 4.6)

1. Place all bulk substrate ingredients into the painter's bucket (Figure 4.6E). Ensure the manure is thoroughly mulched. Use gardening scissors to chop the manure into fine mulch (Figure 4.6D), or use your hands to break up and crumble the clumps. Coconut fiber can be added as a section of compressed brick. It will expand as it soaks up water inside the bucket.

2. Bring the water to a rolling boil on the stove, and hold it there for one minute.

3. Pour the boiling water on top of the dry ingredients in the bucket (Figure 4.6F). Use a wooden spoon to give the mixture a thorough stir (Figure 4.6G), and then fasten down the bucket lid.

4. After one hour, open the lid and thoroughly stir the ingredients again.

5. Refit the bucket lid and leave to cool completely (three to four hours).

6. Once the bulk substrate has cooled, remove the lid and give it a final stir to

ensure even consistency. Ensure the water content is correct by testing the field capacity of the mixture (see page 55).

7. The bulk substrate is now ready to be mixed with grain spawn.

Figure 4.6. Bulk substrate pasteurization—bucket method

4.7 GUIDE: BULK SUBSTRATE PASTEURIZATION—STOVE-TOP METHOD

A more thorough level of pasteurization can be achieved using the following method. The goal is to heat the bulk substrate to 60–65°C (140–149°F) and maintain that temperature for a full hour. Don't allow the temperature to vary beyond that range. Insufficient heating could result in inadequate pasteurization, whereas excessive heating could cause partial sterilization. Both situations can lead to poor bulk substrate performance, so be sure to keep the internal temperature within 60–65°C (140–149°F).

Packing the bulk substrate mixture into a polypropylene bag is efficient because it minimizes mess and allows us to pasteurize a large volume of substrate at once. Note, however, that this method can also be carried out using jars to hold the substrate mixture. When jars are used, the initial heating time is reduced to allow for the comparatively smaller volume of substrate held in each jar.

Materials
- Pressure cooker base (or a large stock pot)
- Polypropylene bag (e.g., a large spawn bag) or canning jars
- Ziploc ties
- Meat thermometer (digital or analog)
- Bulk substrate ingredients
- Large bucket

Method—Pasteurizing in a Bag (see Figure 4.7.1)

1. Mix the bulk substrate ingredients in a large bucket. Ensure the manure is broken up well. Coconut fiber can be added as a portion of brick.

2. Add cold tap water to the bucket. Use a wooden spoon to mix the water through the dry ingredients (Figure 4.7.1B). Allow the mixture to sit for one hour so the water is absorbed. After one hour, mix again to ensure even consistency.

   Test the field capacity of the bulk substrate mixture, and adjust water content as necessary.

3. Pack the bulk substrate mixture firmly into a polypropylene bag, and seal the bag with a Ziploc tie (Figure 4.7.1D). A large spawn bag can be used. Afterward, keep the spawn bag, and reuse it for this task in the future.

4. Place the canning rack into the base of the pressure cooker, and then place the bag of bulk substrate into the pressure cooker.

5. Place the pressure cooker on the stove top and fill it with water until the bag of substrate is halfway submerged (Figure 4.7.1E).

6. Push the meat thermometer probe into the bulk substrate through a point at the top of the bag (Figure 4.7.1H). We want to monitor the temperature of the bulk substrate in the very center. If you are using a digital thermometer, place the digital display unit on the bench next to the stove top and ensure the cord is held up and away from the stove burner.

7. Loosely fit the lid to the pressure cooker. Don't fasten the lid (Figure 4.7.1I). Turn on the stove. Monitor the temperature as it rises. It will take anywhere from twenty minutes to over an hour for the bulk substrate to heat up, depending on the volume of substrate.

8. When the temperature reaches 54°C (130°F), turn off the stove burner. The temperature inside the bag will continue to rise. Note that this timing works consistently for a 6 L (6.3 qt) volume of substrate mixture.

9. Start a timer set to one hour from the moment the internal temperature reaches 60°C (140°F). If the temperature starts to cool, turn the stove top back on for several minutes to keep the internal temperature as close to 60–65°C (140–149°F) as possible.

After an hour, remove the bag of substrate, and allow it to cool for approximately four to five hours. Once cooled, the bulk substrate is ready to be mixed with grain spawn.

Figure 4.7.1. Stove-top pasteurization—bags

Method—Pasteurizing in Jars (see Figure 4.7.2)

1. Follow steps 1 and 2 in the previous method to hydrate the bulk substrate mixture. Pack the mixture firmly into canning jars (Figure 4.7.2B).

2. Cover the mouth of each jar with foil, and then screw a jar-lid ring down to hold the foil in place (Figure 4.7.2C).

3. Place the canning rack and jars of substrate into the pressure cooker. Place the pressure cooker onto the stove top, and fill it with water until the jars are halfway submerged (Figure 4.7.2D).

4. Push the thermometer probe through the foil into the center of one of the jars of substrate (Figure 4.7.2E).

5. Loosely fit the pressure cooker lid, and turn on the stove burner.

6. When the thermometer reads about 40°C (104°F), turn off the stove. The temperature inside the jars will continue to rise. It should take roughly ten to fifteen min to reach 40°C (104°F).

7. Start a timer set to one hour from the moment the internal temperature reaches 60°C (140°F). If the temperature starts to cool, simply turn the stove back on for several minutes to keep the internal temperature as close to 60–65°C (140–149°F) as possible.

After an hour, remove the jars of substrate and allow them to cool for approximately two to three hours. Once cooled, the bulk substrate is ready to be mixed with grain spawn.

Figure 4.7.2. Stove-top pasteurization—jars

4.8 GUIDE: ESTIMATING FIELD CAPACITY

The term *field capacity* is used in soil science, and refers to the maximum amount of water a particular type of soil can hold after excess water has drained away. The ratio and type of ingredients included in the bulk substrate mixture will affect its field capacity.

1. Scoop up a handful of thoroughly mixed bulk substrate. When you hold it in your open hand, it should feel moist, but there should be no excess water dripping out or running between your fingers (Figure 4.8A).

2. Give the handful of bulk substrate a light squeeze. You should see a few dribbles and drips of water run between your fingers (Figure 4.8B).

3. Now, clench your fist tightly. You should see a stream of water run from your fist and between your fingers (Figure 4.8C). Bulk substrate that matches this description is at field capacity, and has perfect water content.

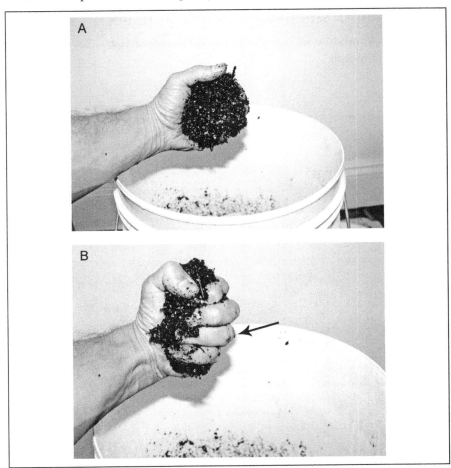

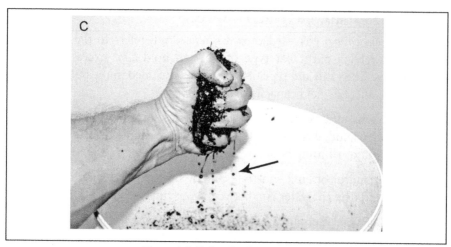

Figure 4.8. Estimating field capacity

4.9 GUIDE: BULK SUBSTRATE—SPAWNING TO BULK

Bulk substrate mixture will be combined with colonized grain spawn in the base of the monotub.

Materials
- Monotub
- Thick plastic sheeting or a large, durable garbage bag
- Pasteurized bulk substrate mixture
- Grain spawn

Equipment and materials for spawning to bulk

Method (see Figure 4.9)

1. Cover all FAE holes with tape (Figure 4.9A).

2. Line the inside of the monotub with plastic sheeting as shown (Figure 4.9B). Fold the plastic into position, and tape it against the sides of the monotub.

   Opaque plastic is used to block light from reaching the sides and bottom of the substrate, thus preventing pins forming on these surfaces during the fruiting stage. We prefer all mushroom growth to occur on the topmost surface of the substrate.

3. Pour half of the bulk substrate mixture into the fruiting chamber, and spread it to all corners (Figure 4.9C).

4. Next, pour the entire volume of grain spawn into the monotub, and spread it to all corners (Figure 4.9D).

   Smell the grain as it's opened. Grain spawn should smell only of healthy mushroom mycelium. Anything other than a clean mushroom scent indicates contamination. Discard any grain that shows a hint of contamination.

5. Add the remaining bulk substrate mixture to the tub, and use your gloved hands to thoroughly blend the spawn and bulk substrate together (Figure 4.9E). Ensure an even depth. Pat the mixture down and level it with your hands, but avoid compressing it.

6. Trim the plastic lining as necessary to ensure it is level with the top of the substrate (Figure 4.9G). Remove any tape that was used to hold the plastic in place.

7. Fit the lid onto the tub, and then place the monotub somewhere out of the way, preferably up off the floor (Figure 4.9I). Allow the monotub to colonize and consolidate completely. A blanket can be thrown over the monotub for insulation (Figure 4.9J).

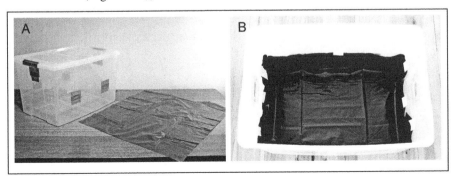

Figure 4.9. Spawning to bulk

The surface of this bulk substrate is 100-percent covered with mycelium. A casing layer can be applied now, or it can be left uncased and allowed to consolidate before introducing fruiting conditions.

4.10 DISCUSSION: BULK SUBSTRATE—COLONIZATION

There are two distinct stages of monotub operation: colonization and fruiting. During the colonization stage, we set conditions inside the monotub to be optimal for vegetative growth. Mushroom spawn is allowed to expand and colonize the entire bulk substrate. We can watch its progression as white mycelium gradually colonizes every portion of the bulk substrate, eventually covering the substrate surface entirely.

Consolidation

Even after the substrate surface is entirely covered with white mycelium, we must continue to wait while the mycelium colonizes all the resources inside the substrate, a process referred to as *consolidation*. This is the last stage of colonization, where the mycelium really takes hold of the substrate.

Often, a fully consolidated substrate will actually start to show signs of fruit formation even before fruiting conditions have been introduced. Many growers wait to see the earliest stages of fruit formation on the substrate before switching to fruiting conditions because they believe that it's best to let the mycelium indicate on its own when it's ready to fruit.

We usually allow an extra five to ten days after the surface of the substrate is 100-percent covered with white mycelium for the substrate to consolidate. Allowing for this, we can expect the entire process of colonization and consolidation to take anywhere from fourteen to thirty days. However long it takes, it is important not to rush into fruiting conditions. Prematurely switching to fruiting conditions before the substrate is completely colonized and consolidated can result in an uneven or poor pin set, and an otherwise sub-optimal first flush of fruit. A substrate that has been allowed to consolidate thoroughly will usually provide a better first flush.

Conditions inside the Fruiting Chamber

Conditions inside the monotub should remain perfect for colonization, with no need for further input from us. We are aiming to simulate the conditions mycelium would experience in a natural setting, as it grows inside dung or topsoil for example. During colonization, the monotub should be left alone as much as possible. It doesn't hurt to open the lid a bit every few days to see how things are progressing; however, avoid removing the lid completely, for this will affect the balance of conditions we are trying to achieve inside the chamber. Factors that should be considered during colonization include the following:

GE

During colonization, we aim to keep the CO_2 levels inside the monotub higher than ambient. We achieve this by sealing the FAE holes in the sides of the fruiting chamber to restrict air movement.

Although elevated CO_2 levels are required, it is important that CO_2 not be allowed to build up to a concentration where it actually becomes inhibitory to mycelial growth. Therefore, a certain amount of GE is required to allow excess CO_2 to dissipate and to allow oxygen to enter the fruiting chamber. The plastic tubs we use to construct the monotub usually don't have airtight lids, and sufficient GE is able to occur around the edge of the lid. If necessary, GE can be increased by leaving one FAE hole uncovered and stuffed tightly with filter material during colonization.

Humidity

High humidity contributes to vigorous and healthy mycelial growth by allowing the mycelium to be fully hydrated. High humidity is a requirement during both the colonization and fruiting stages of monotub operation.

Humidity inside the monotub is maintained by evaporation from the substrate itself. Ambient conditions and air movement into the monotub can also influence humidity. During the colonization stage, there should be minimal air movement so that little (if any) moisture is lost from the system. Later, when we introduce fruiting conditions, we must take steps to preserve high humidity in the presence of increased airflow into the chamber.

It is possible to gauge humidity simply by observing the level of condensation inside the fruiting chamber. When condensation is clearly observable—lining the walls and underside of the lid and/or beading on exposed mycelium on the surface of the substrate—we can safely assume humidity is suitable.

Condensation lining the inside of the monotub indicates suitable humidity

Temperature
Bulk substrate should colonize successfully at normal room temperatures. The optimum temperature range is slightly cooler for colonizing bulk substrate than it is for grain spawn. Around 21–25°C (70–78°F) is best. Be aware that colonizing bulk substrate generates a good deal of its own heat, more so than grain spawn, simply because of the greater volume of spawn. Keep this in mind when considering temperature.

Lighting
Lighting requirements for colonizing bulk substrate are very flexible. As with grain spawn, the bulk substrate should colonize perfectly well in light or dark conditions. Typical household lighting or indirect sunlight is fine. Overly bright lighting and direct sunlight should be avoided.

Contamination and Poor Performance
Ideally, colonization should proceed steadily until the entire bulk substrate is covered by white mycelium. Once fully colonized, a bulk substrate is quite resistant to contamination, and we'll often be able to harvest multiple flushes of fruit over several weeks without contamination interfering. Unfortunately, it's not always smooth sailing, and we may occasionally experience problems with the substrate becoming prematurely contaminated. Common causes of poor bulk substrate performance and/or premature contamination are listed below, along with possible solutions.

As with grain spawn, contamination on bulk substrate can take the form of any kind of growth that isn't white mycelium. In addition, some kinds of mold can be white and have a similar appearance to mycelium. Smell is an accurate indicator of contamination.

Most of the contaminants in a residential house are located at floor-level, where dust often accumulates. Therefore, if you have trouble with contamination, store the monotub on a shelf or bench and avoid storing your substrate close to the floor. Households that allow pets indoors will have a generally higher level of airborne contaminants floating around. Keep pets out of your grow room as much as possible.

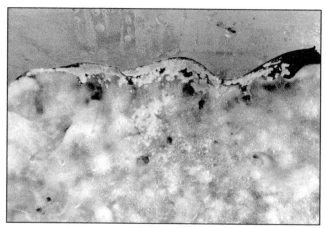

Mold growing on a colonizing bulk substrate

Contaminated Grain Spawn

If a properly pasteurized bulk substrate becomes contaminated before the first flush, the cause is likely to be contaminated grain spawn. Be absolutely certain that the grain spawn mixed with bulk substrate is healthy and contaminant free. Any contaminants carried over with grain will thrive in the bulk substrate mixture, and will most likely ruin the grow.

Improper pasteurization of substrate

Inadequate pasteurization can lead to bulk substrate becoming contaminated quickly. To avoid this, ensure ingredients are thoroughly broken up before pasteurization. If you have persistent contamination problems when using the bucket method, consider using the more thorough stove-top pasteurization method detailed in this book (page 51).

The opposite situation, in which bulk substrate is partially sterilized as a result of having been treated at too high of a temperature, can also lead to premature contamination. When conducting a thorough pasteurization of bulk substrate, be sure that temperatures don't exceed 65°C (149°F) for longer than five minutes. Note that partial sterilization is unlikely to occur when using the bucket method of pasteurization.

Incorrect water content

Incorrect water content can lead to problems. Too much water in the bulk substrate can cause slow mycelial growth and may create anaerobic conditions favorable to some kinds of bacteria, thus leading to contamination.

On the other hand, a substrate with inadequate water content will be unable to maintain high humidity inside the fruiting chamber, causing mycelium to be dehydrated and stressed. Extremely dry conditions can cause bruising, revealed as blueing of exposed mycelium. Stressed mycelium may show slow growth rates, poor fruit formation, and reduced yield.

Water content can't really be fixed after you have spawned to bulk. Ideally, you need to aim for perfect water content when preparing bulk substrate mixture. Always aim for bulk substrate to be at field capacity when estimating water content.

Insufficient grain spawn

Including insufficient spawn when spawning to bulk can result in a slow rate of colonization. In turn, this may allow contaminants to become established. Definitely aim for grain spawn to account for no less than 30 percent of the total grain spawn–bulk substrate mixture. If you experience slow rates of colonization, aim for grain spawn to account for 40–50 percent of total volume.

Insufficient GE

Excessive CO_2 buildup or insufficient oxygen can suffocate and slow mycelial growth. Again, slow colonization increases the likelihood of contaminants getting a foothold. Correct low rates of GE by loosely fitting the monotub lid, and removing the tape from one of the bottom FAE holes and replacing it with tightly packed filter material.

Low Temperatures

Extremely low temperatures can cause slow colonization. If your ambient temperature is suboptimal, you can insulate the fruiting chamber by covering it with a blanket, warm the grow room with a heater, or use a seedling-propagation mat to warm the monotub from underneath. If using a heat mat be sure to raise the fruiting chamber with spacers. This will allow excess heat to dissipate and prevent possible overheating.

Overlay

Overlay is a unique situation where mycelium overcolonizes the surface of the substrate and casing layer, forming a thick mat. Although it is uncommon, it is most likely to occur if the substrate is kept in colonizing conditions for too long. In the absence of triggers that stimulate a switch from vegetative growth to fruit production, the mycelium continues to grow in a vegetative state, forming a thick layer. A bulk substrate that has experienced overlay may still produce fruit when exposed to fruiting conditions. Avoid overlay by initiating fruiting conditions at the proper time once the substrate is fully colonized and consolidated.

Poor Genetics

A slow growth rate may be a result of genetics, a variable that is impossible to predict when growing from a spore print. See page 105 for a discussion of mushroom genetics.

Dealing with Contamination on Bulk Substrate

Small, localized patches of mold can be removed from a bulk substrate or casing layer if identified early enough. The contaminated area is scooped out with a sterilized spoon and discarded. The exposed area can then be covered in a layer of table salt to suppress the growth of any remaining mold spores for long enough to get a flush of fruit from the remainder of the uncontaminated substrate. This method is useful only for treating small areas of contamination and isn't always successful.

Scoop the mold out with a sterilized spoon

Cover the area with table salt

4.11 DISCUSSION: GE VERSUS FAE

At this point, let's take a moment to clarify the difference between gas exchange (GE) and fresh air exchange (FAE). To a beginner, these two processes may seem difficult to differentiate, both being to do with the movement of air and gases. Although they are certainly related, they perform different functions and are relevant at different stages of the growing process.

GE

In the biological sciences, GE refers to the process by which the respiratory gases (oxygen and CO_2) move in opposite directions between a living organism's external environment and its internal cellular environment via its respiratory organs.

In the context of magic mushroom cultivation, however, GE has a slightly nuanced meaning. When we refer to GE, we usually aren't talking about the process of GE in the fungal organism itself, but rather the movement of gases (again, oxygen and CO_2) between an enclosed growing container (e.g., a grain jar, grain bag, or fruiting chamber) and the external environment. Obviously, the strict definition and our use of the term are implicitly related, but they aren't one and the same. This book assumes the latter definition when referring to GE.

GE, as we use the term, is a passive process, relying on gases to move by themselves via diffusion from areas of high to low concentration through a vent in the growing container. This process occurs in grain jars and bags via filtered vents, and in the monotub fruiting chamber via the crack where the lid meets the tub or via an exposed, filtered FAE hole. The purpose of GE, as we define it, is to prevent the buildup of CO_2 inside the growing container to levels that can inhibit mycelial growth and to allow oxygen to enter, which is essential for mycelium to grow.

FAE

By comparison, FAE is a process we introduce to a completely colonized bulk substrate to stimulate mycelium to switch from a state of vegetative growth to fruit production. FAE involves allowing fresh air to enter the fruiting chamber from the external environment.

We can usually get sufficient FAE into the fruiting chamber simply by way of natural air currents circulating in the grow room. Alternatively, a fan can be used to increase air movement and force fresh air into the fruiting chamber. Stale air is expelled from the fruiting chamber in the process. This movement of air results in an equalization of gases between the interior of the fruiting chamber and the external environment.

Dissipation of CO_2 that has been allowed to build up during colonization of the bulk substrate is a key fruiting condition that helps trigger the production of mushrooms. In addition, FAE increases evaporation from the surface of the substrate, which is another condition that stimulates fruit production.

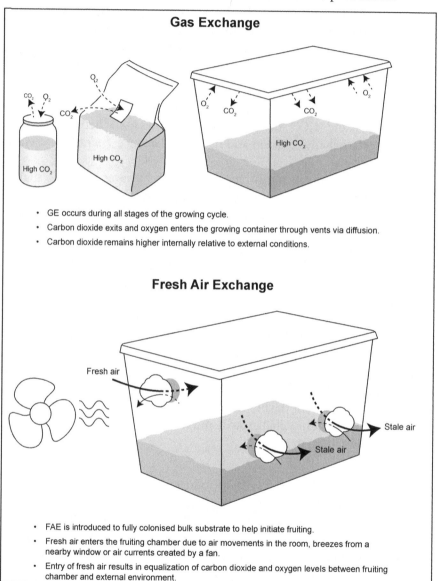

Gas Exchange

- GE occurs during all stages of the growing cycle.
- Carbon dioxide exits and oxygen enters the growing container through vents via diffusion.
- Carbon dioxide remains higher internally relative to external conditions.

Fresh Air Exchange

- FAE is introduced to fully colonised bulk substrate to help initiate fruiting.
- Fresh air enters the fruiting chamber due to air movements in the room, breezes from a nearby window or air currents created by a fan.
- Entry of fresh air results in equalization of carbon dioxide and oxygen levels between fruiting chamber and external environment.

4.12 DISCUSSION: CASING LAYERS

Traditionally, a casing layer is defined as a layer of non nutritious material placed across the top of a bulk substrate. The desire is for mycelium to grow through the layer, but for it to not actively digest the layer. The purpose of a casing layer is to supply moisture to the growing mycelium and to create a humid and aerated microclimate at the surface of the substrate that will stimulate the formation of mushrooms. Peat moss, vermiculite, and coconut fiber are examples of materials traditionally used in casing layers. Additives such as gypsum and hydrated lime can be included to provide minerals to developing fruit and to buffer pH.

Many opinions exist about the benefit (or lack thereof) of using a casing layer when growing *P. cubensis*. The prevalent view is that a casing layer is unnecessary, and it is certainly true that excellent yields can be achieved without one. Despite this, many growers still apply casing layers based on the belief they can help achieve an even pin set, which helps contribute to producing higher yields. Ultimately, it becomes a personal preference, which can be determined by priorities. If you want to proceed quickly with as few steps as possible, you can safely elect to skip a casing layer.

A casing layer is applied when colonization of the substrate is complete, before the introduction of fruiting conditions. After application of a casing layer, an additional two to five days of colonization are allowed before the bulk substrate is placed into fruiting conditions.

4.13 GUIDE: APPLYING A CASING LAYER

Materials
- 50% coconut fiber
- 50% vermiculite
- 0.4 L water for every 1 L of casing mixture

Method—Estimating Volumes
Aim for the casing layer to be about 1.5 cm thick (0.5 in). Using our monotub from previous examples the volumes of ingredients can be calculated as follows:

$$50 \text{ cm} \times 30 \text{ cm} \times 1.5 \text{ cm} = 2{,}250 \text{ mL}$$

Knowing the total volume of casing mixture, we can calculate the required amount of each ingredient:

Coconut fiber = (2,250 mL / 100) × 50% = 1,125 mL (=1.125 L or 1.2 qt)
Vermiculite = (2,250 mL / 100) × 50% = 1,125 mL (=1.125 L or 1.2 qt)
Water = 2,250 L × 0.4 L = 0.9 L (0.95 qt)

Method (see Figure 4.13)

1. Tip dry ingredients into a bucket.

2. Pasteurize and hydrate the casing layer by using one of the two methods previously discussed.

3. Sprinkle the cooled casing material over the top of the bulk substrate, ensuring an even depth of 1.5 cm (0.5 in) (Figure 4.13C).

4. Allow an additional two to five days of colonization. Initiate fruiting conditions once mycelium can be seen emerging evenly through 20–30 percent of the casing layer.

If you observe that an uneven pattern of mycelial growth has grown up through the casing layer, lightly patch over the vigorously growing areas with casing material, then wait another day or two before fruiting.

Figure 4.13. Applying a casing layer

Roughly five days after application of the casing layer, uneven areas of growth are patched with casing material.

After patching, allow another few days of colonization before introducing fruiting conditions.

CHAPTER 5

Fruiting

We are now reaching the most exciting stage of the grow, when we will be rewarded for all our hard work. We have allowed our bulk substrate to colonize and consolidate, and now it is time to switch to fruiting conditions and watch a small forest of mushrooms bloom.

5.1 DISCUSSION: FRUITING BULK SUBSTRATE

Initiate fruiting conditions when the bulk substrate has completely colonized, and has been allowed to consolidate. We can initiate fruiting conditions just before the earliest signs of fruit formation, or we can wait until we can actually see hyphal knots forming on the substrate. By waiting until we see early signs of fruit formation, we can be absolutely sure that the substrate is fully colonized and ready to fruit.

If a casing layer was applied, the formation of hyphal knots will be obscured from view. In this case, introduce fruiting conditions as soon as mycelium can be seen growing evenly through 20–30 percent of the casing layer.

The entire fruiting process should take approximately two weeks from the time fruiting conditions are introduced to the formation of mature mushrooms.

The first stages of fruit formation look like tiny white dots forming on strands of exposed mycelium. On an uncased substrate, these tiny hyphal knots should be easy to see. If a casing layer was used, the hyphal knots will form inside the casing layer and may be obscured from view as a result. Hyphal knots should begin to form en masse after introducing fruiting conditions. Hyphal knots gradually grow larger and become recognizable as tiny mushrooms. At this stage, they are referred to as *pins*, or *primordia*. The distribution of pins across the substrate is referred to as the *pin set*.

Fully colonized and consolidated bulk substrate ready for fruiting

This cased substrate is ready for fruiting, for mycelium can be seen emerging evenly through 20–30 percent of the casing layer.

Fruiting Conditions

Fruiting conditions are stimuli that act to trigger the formation of fruit from the bulk substrate. In a natural setting, *P. cubensis* mushrooms often form shortly after rain. Mycelium growing inside a suitable substrate, such as animal dung, is stimulated to produce fruit where the mycelium intersects the surface of the dung substrate and becomes exposed to external conditions. Exposure to light and fresh air, increased humidity, evaporation from the soil surface, and a drop in temperature at ground level all stimulate fruit formation. When fruiting our bulk substrate, we aim to create an artificial approximation of these conditions inside the monotub.

Fully colonized substrate

Complete colonization and consolidation of the substrate is an important fruiting trigger. Once the mycelium has fully utilized all available resources, it responds by changing to a state of reproduction (i.e., production of mushrooms). A fully colonized and consolidated bulk substrate will begin to show signs of fruiting without any encouragement from us. Therefore full colonization of the substrate is a required condition for successful fruiting.

FAE

The movement of fresh air into the monotub has the effect of dissipating CO_2 that was allowed to build up during the colonization stage. This drop in CO_2 concentration is an important fruiting trigger. The more fresh air we can circulate into the fruiting chamber the better, provided we can maintain high humidity.

FAE is achieved by uncovering the monotub's FAE holes thus allowing fresh air to enter the fruiting chamber. In most cases, sufficient airflow into the fruiting chamber will occur passively due to air currents in the room. An open window can aid movement of fresh air into the grow room while an electric fan can be used to circulate air in the grow room and increase airflow into the fruiting chamber. FAE can also be increased by periodically (once a day for example) using the lid to fan air into the interior of the fruiting chamber.

Evaporation

A steady rate of evaporation from the surface of the substrate is an important fruiting trigger. Water droplets beading on the surface of the substrate and on the mycelium itself will evaporate into the air at a steady rate due to the increased airflow in the fruiting chamber. It is important that the surface of the substrate not be allowed to dry out in the presence of steady evaporation and increased FAE. Moisture content from the substrate should be sufficient to allow for steady evaporation, but additional misting may be required.

Light

Light hitting the surface of the substrate triggers hyphal knot formation, helps provide an even pin set, and contributes to generally bigger and healthier mushrooms. Light can be in the form of indirect sunlight from a window or artificial lighting.

It is important that light be directed evenly across the surface of the substrate as much as possible. Uneven spread of light onto the substrate may result in uneven distribution of fruit. If using artificial lighting, aim to simulate a twelve-hour day/night cycle. This can be automated using a timer to turn the lamp on and off at predefined intervals. A globe emitting light in the range of 6,000–7,000 K is best.

Note that the plastic lining we placed into the bottom of the monotub when spawning to bulk is intended to block light from reaching the sides and bottom of the substrate. This prevents pins from forming on these surfaces, and ensures that all fruit forms on the upper surface.

Humidity

High humidity is important for all stages of fruit formation and development. It can be a challenge to maintain high humidity in the presence of increased airflow and evaporation. A balance must be achieved between adequate FAE and preserving high humidity at the surface of the substrate. Excessive moisture loss is prevented by filling FAE holes with filter material. If necessary, humidity can be increased by misting the walls of the fruiting chamber; however, our goal is for the humidity to be as self-regulating as possible.

Application of a casing layer can help maintain high humidity at the surface of the substrate. Water droplets clinging to exposed mycelium on an uncased substrate tell us that humidity at the surface of the substrate is perfect for fruit formation.

Tiny droplets of moisture are an indication that humidity at the surface of the substrate is suitable for fruit formation.

Temperature

Psilocybe cubensis can successfully fruit in a wide range of temperatures. It isn't, therefore, essential to take any special steps to manage temperature when switching to fruiting conditions. We'll certainly obtain an excellent crop simply by leaving the monotub at the same temperature at which it colonized. However, aiming for a slightly cooler temperature during fruiting can result in a denser crop, and fruit that is potentially more potent. For this reason, to achieve the best results during the fruiting stage, aim to store your monotub at 20–24°C (68–75°F), which is slightly cooler than for colonizing bulk substrate.

5.2 GUIDE: FRUITING BULK SUBSTRATE

To initiate fruiting we will remove the tape from the FAE holes and replace it with filters made from synthetic cushion filler (Poly-Fil). The filters allow air movement and prevent excessive moisture loss from the interior of the fruiting chamber. The four bottom holes are packed tightly to make them more resistant to airflow. The two top holes are packed loosely. Arranging the filter densities in this way allows greater airflow through the two higher holes and preserves humidity at the surface of the substrate. Air entering through the upper holes circulates inside the chamber, dissipating built-up CO_2 and causing increased evaporation from the substrate.

Method (see Figure 5.2)

1. Remove tape from all FAE holes (Figure 5.2B).

2. Pack filter material loosely into the top two FAE holes.

   Tease out a piece of synthetic cushion filler into a thin layer (Figure 5.2C). Roll it into a loose ball (Figure 5.2D), and sit it lightly into one of the top FAE holes (Figure 5.2F). Repeat to fill the second hole.

3. Pack filter material tightly into the four bottom holes. Use twice as much filter material as for the filters in the upper holes (Figure 5.2G).

4. Position the monotub where it will receive indirect sunlight (Figure 5.2I). If using artificial lights, implement the simulated natural lighting schedule of twelve hours on, twelve hours off.

5. An open window should facilitate ample FAE. Alternatively, a fan can be positioned in the room to circulate air and increase rates of FAE.

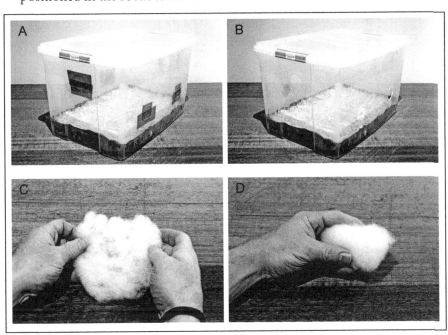

Figure 5.2. Fruiting bulk substrate

5.3 DISCUSSION: FRUIT FORMATION (...PINS! ...PINS EVERYWHERE!)

Over the course of the grow, we've taken steps to facilitate the formation of an even pin set across the surface of the substrate. Now, as the pins emerge, we can see if we've successfully achieved our goal. Steps such as mixing spawn and bulk substrate evenly, ensuring an even depth of bulk substrate and casing layer, patching the casing layer, consolidating the substrate before fruiting, and ensuring correct humidity at the substrate surface are all designed to encourage uniform mycelial growth and a corresponding even spread of fruit.

Even distribution of fruit across the surface of the substrate is desirable because it represents the most efficient and productive use of available space, and makes for an easier harvest. It is preferable for fruit to reach maturity uniformly, as opposed to having fruit at varying stages of maturity.

Mushrooms will grow steadily larger over successive days, and a point will come when the fruit seems to double in size overnight. The caps will open and separate from the annulus and, before you know it, the time will have come to harvest the first flush.

Mushroom formation

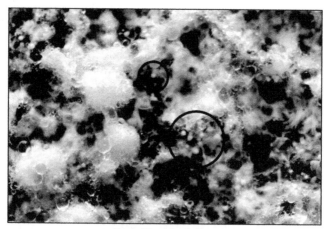

Hyphal knot formation

Hyphal knots develop into tiny primordia/pins

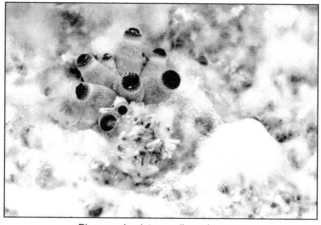

Pins growing into small mushrooms

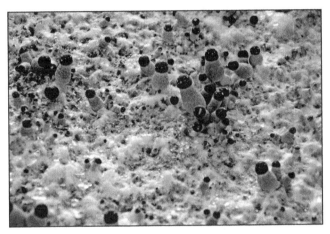

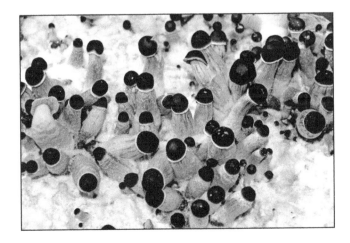

Small mushrooms

Small and medium sized mushrooms

Mature mushrooms

Bulk substrate covered with mature fruit, removed from the fruiting chamber

A dense canopy of fruit ready for harvest

5.4 DISCUSSION: MONOTUB OPERATION—FRUITING

Successful monotub operation during the fruiting stage relies on achieving a balance between the various fruiting conditions. We need to keep a close eye on conditions inside the fruiting chamber and make corrections to the monotub setup if necessary.

If the monotub has been set up correctly we should have a self-regulating system that will require very little further input from us. Fresh air should be circulating into the fruiting chamber, pushing stale air out and causing equalized CO_2 levels and increased evaporation from the substrate surface. Filters prevent excessive moisture loss and thereby preserve humidity levels. A small amount of moisture will inevitably be lost from the system but this can easily be replenished by misting if necessary.

Note that ambient conditions may influence your growing environment. If you live in a place where the air is very dry, you may need to set up your monotub to better conserve humidity. On the other hand, if you live in a very humid environment, you may be able to operate your monotub with no filters at all in the top holes, and still maintain perfect humidity inside. It may take some trial and error to achieve the best settings for your local conditions.

Possible Problems During Fruiting

While we aim for the monotub to be self-regulating as much as possible, problems can arise during fruiting if conditions aren't balanced correctly. In that case we may need to change the monotub setup or take a more active role by providing additional fanning or misting. In some cases, we may get poor fruit formation even when conditions are perfect, simply due to poor genetics.

Aborts

Mushrooms that fail to develop beyond small pins into mature, full-sized fruit are called aborts. Aborted pins are easy to identify as they often develop discoloured, almost black caps. It is normal for every flush to have a few aborts; however, occasionally, if something goes wrong, we can have excessively high numbers of aborts. In such cases, we need to look closely at our growing environment to identify possible problems.

There are a number of reasons why mushrooms may abort in large numbers. A sudden change in humidity or temperature is a common cause, as is CO_2 buildup resulting from inadequate FAE. Misting water directly onto pins can also cause them to abort.

Very heavy pin sets can sometimes have a higher-than-usual number of aborts if the substrate is unable to provide adequate nutrition to the developing fruit. In this situation, if the mycelium is unable to derive adequate resources from the substrate to support the developing fruit, some will be forced to abort.

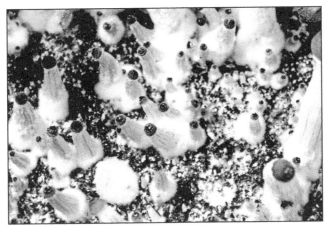
Aborted pins

Low humidity

Low humidity inside the fruiting chamber causes the substrate surface to dry out. Hyphal knots may not form or develop into pins in the presence of low humidity, and those pins that do form may abort soon after forming. In dry conditions, pin sets may be sparse and uneven. We may see pins forming in the corners, along the edges of the substrate, or in depressions, where the microclimate is most humid. Mushrooms that do develop may be slow growing, have small caps or be small in size overall, or develop cracks on their caps.

Low humidity can be caused by too much airflow into the chamber. In other words, we will have been too aggressive with FAE. Possible reasons for this could be that the filters were applied too loosely or that running a fan in the room pushed too much air into the chamber.

To avoid this situation, monitor condensation inside the monotub during fruiting to identify declining humidity before it becomes a problem. The inside walls and underside of the lid should remain covered in beads of condensation. Also, the surface of the substrate itself should always have a fine coating of condensation. You may notice dry rings surrounding the FAE holes but this is to be expected because of the increased air movement at these points.

Declining humidity can be corrected by misting (once a day, for example). Use a spray bottle to mist water onto the walls of the fruiting chamber. Avoid misting the substrate or fruit directly. To better preserve humidity, reduce airflow into the chamber by packing FAE filters more tightly (especially the bottom holes), and ensure that any airflow from a fan isn't pointed directly at the monotub. You may elect to cease operation of a fan altogether. Getting the level of humidity right isn't an exact science, and you will need to adjust your methods to suit your local conditions.

Monotub insufficiently aerated (low FAE)

Inadequate FAE can seriously hamper pin set and fruit formation. A steady rate of evaporation from the substrate is required for pins to form, and evaporation is dependent on adequate movement of air into the fruiting chamber. Also, if the interior of the monotub is insufficiently aerated, CO_2 may not adequately dissipate. This can lead to development of poorly formed fruit. Mushrooms with tall, spindly stems or convoluted, twisted shapes indicate CO_2 buildup at the surface of the substrate resulting from insufficient FAE. Insufficient FAE can be corrected by taking all or some of the following steps:

- Reduce the thickness of the filters. You may even elect to remove filters from the topmost holes altogether.

- Ensure that fresh air is able to enter the grow room from an open window or from adjoining rooms.

- Regularly fan the inside of the fruiting chamber. Remove the lid and use it to fan fresh air into the monotub once a day, for example.

- Operate a fan in the grow room. Direct the current of air to pass close by, but not directly toward the monotub.

- Be sure that the bottom edge of the lowest FAE holes are around 2–4 cm (0.8–1.5 in) from the substrate surface.

When implementing these corrections, always pay attention to humidity. Humidity and FAE are linked, and corrections to one will affect the other. Successful monotub operation relies on balancing these conditions. If you notice the walls of the monotub drying out because of the extra airflow, mist the monotub to maintain high humidity.

Poor or uneven pin set

Ideally, we hope to achieve a dense, evenly spaced distribution of fruit across the surface of the substrate that will mature at roughly the same rate and grow to occupy the available space completely. However, sometimes this doesn't happen. Instead we see a sporadic or sparse pattern of growth as pins begin to form. There can be a few reasons for an uneven pin set.

As described throughout this chapter, environmental conditions (e.g., humidity, FAE, and light) can influence the pin set. High humidity at the surface of the substrate is essential for hyphal knot formation and their subsequent development into pins. FAE has a direct bearing on humidity, and it must be optimized in order to preserve humidity while simultaneously facilitating increased evaporation—another key fruiting trigger. An even distribution of light onto the substrate is important for the development of a good pin set. Exceedingly dim light or no light at all may result in a poorly developed pin set. These conditions must therefore be optimized to give the best chance of producing a good pin set.

Premature introduction of fruiting conditions before the substrate has been allowed to consolidate fully can result in an uneven pin set. This is because fully colonized parts of the substrate will be readily stimulated to produce fruit, while less thoroughly colonized portions of the substrate may remain in a vegetative state of growth. Always ensure that the substrate has been allowed to fully colonize and consolidate before introducing fruiting conditions.

Finally, even if all other conditions have been perfectly optimized, a poor pin set may still occur, purely as a result of genetic variability. When growing from a spore print, we simply can't determine the particular traits that will be inherent to our crop. We can improve the consistency and predictability of the pin set and fruit formation by growing from clones and isolating strains that display favorable fruiting characteristics.

CHAPTER 6

Harvest Time

When faced with a monotub full of maturing fruit, the first considera-tion—perhaps somewhat counterintuitively—should not be to harvest immediately and organize a camping trip. Instead, we need to think about col-lecting genetic material for future use in the form of spore prints, and possibly also tissue samples.

When collecting spore prints, there is a sense of everything coming full circle. We started with a spore print, and now we have the opportunity to collect multiple spore prints for use in future grows and to preserve a sample of the genetics of our crop.

Although it is possible to continue growing successive crops from our own spore prints indefinitely, we'll eventually want to turn our attention to an alternative strategy of growing from clones and/or isolated strains.

Cloning, or tissue culturing, involves taking a sample of tissue from the inside of a mushroom stem and growing it in isolation on agar. The resulting cultures can then be used to inoculate grain medium, or used as the starting point for a series of transfers to new agar plates in order to isolate a single high-yielding strain. The advantages of growing with clones and isolated strains are discussed in chapter 7, along with a simple methodology for taking clones and making subcultures.

6.1 DISCUSSION: SPORE PRINTS

Spore printing is an easy way to collect genetic material from a crop of mushrooms, and prints should stay viable for up to five years. The method of spore-print collection discussed below can be used to create viable prints for the purpose of grain inoculation, or for the preservation of genetics.

Making a spore print involves slicing the cap off a mushroom, then collecting its spores on a sheet of foil. The aim is to make spore prints that are as clean and as contaminant-free as possible. In practice, it is difficult to make spore prints that are 100-percent free of contaminants due to the fact that the interior of the monotub isn't a sterile environment. Air containing bacteria and mold spores has been able to move freely into the fruiting chamber from the time of spawning to bulk, and the mushroom caps themselves are likely to have contaminants deposited on them from the air.

We minimize the opportunity for contaminants to settle on the spore print by once again practicing aseptic technique, and by choosing mushroom caps that have only recently opened. We're hoping that the underside and gills of the mushrooms, having only recently opened, are as close to contaminant free as possible.

6.2 GUIDE: MAKING SPORE PRINTS

Materials
- Medium-sized container with lid
- Large plastic tub with lid
- Sharp, thin-bladed knife (e.g., a retractable, snap-off–style cutter is best)
- Aluminum foil (heavy duty or extra-thick is best)

Method (see Figure 6.2)

1. While working in your clean area and wearing gloves, wipe out the inside of the two containers with 70 percent isopropanol. Don't forget to wipe the underside of the lids. Flame-sterilize the knife blade.

   The medium-sized container will be used to collect multiple mushroom caps and transport them to the clean area, whereas the large tub will be used to store the mushroom caps while they drop their spores.

2. Cut foil into 8 cm (3 in) squares, put them into an oven dish, and place them in the oven at 180°C (350°F) for ten minutes.

3. Collect multiple mushroom caps. While wearing disposable gloves, grip each cap by the edges, and cut the stem as close as possible to the cap without touching the gills (Figure 6.2B). Transfer each cap to the medium-sized container, and fasten down the lid (Figure 6.2C).

4. In the clean work area, flip the lid of the large plastic tub upside down, and place it on the bench. Place the foil squares onto the lid, arranging them side by side.

5. Place the mushroom caps onto the foil squares (Figure 6.2D), with the gills facing down. Fit the tub upside down onto the lid (Figure 6.2E), and leave the caps alone for twelve to twenty-four hours to allow them to drop their spores.

6. Remove the mushroom caps. They can be dried with the rest of the harvested fruit. You should see a dark spore print on each square of foil (Figure 6.2F). Refit the tub, and leave the prints for an additional hour to dry and set.

7. Once set, the prints are ready to be folded and stored (Figure 6.2G). Label the outside of each print with relevant information (e.g., the date and strain) and store them in a dry, airtight container at room temperature.

Figure 6.2. Making spore prints

6.3 DISCUSSION: HARVESTING

The best time to harvest the crop is shortly after the caps have opened and broken away from the veil. A crop left for too long will become coated in a thick purplish black layer as spores are dropped en masse. A coating of spores won't affect the potency of the fruit; however, if aesthetics is important to you, the harvest should be done shortly after the caps open before spores begin to drop.

The best tool for harvesting your crop is a retractable snap-off-style cutter (Figure 6.3A). The long, thin blade provides the necessary reach to access the base of the stems among a forest of mushrooms. Alternatively, thin-bladed scissors can be used. If possible, remove the substrate from the fruiting chamber, and sit it on a bench (Figure 6.3B).

Cut the mushrooms at the base as close to the substrate as possible. Start at one corner, and work systematically across the substrate (Figure 6.3C), collecting your harvest in a large bucket. In most cases, you won't be cutting individual mushroom stems; rather, you will be cutting large clumps of mycelium composing the base of multiple mushrooms (Figure 6.3D).

If you spot any bulk substrate particles clinging to the stems, knock them back onto the substrate. After removing all the obvious mushrooms, you may wish to do a second pass and pare back some of the bases even closer to the substrate.

If the substrate produced an uneven pin set, you may have fruit at various stages of maturity. In that case, simply remove the caps of the earlier fruit so they don't have a chance to drop spores, and wait for the rest of the crop to catch up.

Figure 6.3. Harvesting

6.4 DISCUSSION: DRYING AND STORAGE

Your bountiful crop should be thoroughly dried and stored in airtight containers. Mushrooms will not last for long if they aren't dried properly because they will become mouldy. A food dehydrator is a highly recommended piece of equipment for drying your crop. It is possible to dry mushrooms using other methods, such as in front of a fan or next to a heater, but, a food dehydrator will do the job much more efficiently. Be sure to purchase a food dehydrator that has both a fan and a heating element.

The crop should be held in the dehydrator until every part of the fruit is crispy and snaps when bent. Pay attention to the flesh in the middle of the cap at the very top of the stem. This spot may take the longest to dry thoroughly. Rotate the racks inside the dehydrator to ensure consistent drying.

Once the mushrooms are thoroughly dry, they can be packed into airtight containers and stored long term. Anything with an airtight lid is suitable for long-term storage.

Food dehydrator with built-in fan and heating element

Dehydrator trays loaded with freshly harvested fruit

Thoroughly dried product after several hours in the dehydrator

Dried fruit can be stored long term in airtight containers

Silica gel

Dried mushrooms should be stored with silica gel desiccant packs in each container to absorb any residual moisture left in the mushrooms or present in the enclosed air. Mushrooms stored this way, and kept away from heat and fresh air, will retain their magic for two to three years or longer.

Silica gel packs may become fully laden with moisture over time. They can be recharged for reuse by putting them into a food dehydrator or an oven for two to three hours. If using an oven, space the gel packs apart on an oven tray, and leave the door a quarter of the way open. Set the oven to a low temperature (100°C/212°F). Once the silica gel packs have been recharged this way, store them in an airtight container until needed.

A silica gel pack

Silica gel absorbs moisture from air enclosed in the storage container

Several silica gel packs should be used for larger containers

Recharging silica packs in a dehydrator

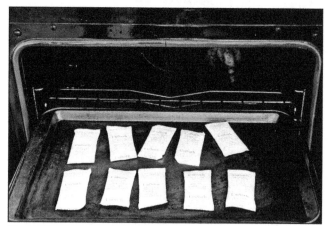

The door should be left ajar when recharging silica packs in an oven

6.5 DISCUSSION: YIELD

Yield is influenced by growing conditions (e.g., substrate volume, substrate ingredients, and fruiting-chamber management) and genetics. Although the grower is able to control growing conditions, genetics introduces a degree of unpredictability when using multispore inoculation. Even when growing conditions are optimized, it can be difficult to predict the yield of a multispore bulk grow.

Despite the inconsistency of multispore crops, it is possible to make some general estimations regarding yield, albeit within a fairly wide range. The first flush from a 12 L (12.7 qt) bulk substrate—such as the one prepared in chapter 4 (page 45) for a theoretical 50 L monotub—could be expected to yield anywhere between two and six ounces of dried mushrooms from its first flush, assuming optimal growing conditions were achieved.

The ability to predict yield with a greater degree of certainty, and to achieve higher yields in general, are major reasons for making the transition to cloning and strain isolation. When growing from a high-yielding isolated strain or clone (as opposed to a multispore inoculation originating from a spore print), it should be possible to consistently achieve four to six ounces or more of dried mushrooms from the first flush of the same 12 L (12.7 qt) substrate.

When measuring yields, we are usually interested in dry weight. As a rule of thumb, dry weight will be around ten percent of the weight of freshly picked fruit, reflecting the fact that mushrooms are about ninety percent water.

6.6 DISCUSSION: ADDITIONAL FLUSHES

It is possible to harvest multiple flushes of fruit from a single bulk substrate. After the first flush is harvested, the substrate is rehydrated and put back into fruiting conditions. New fruit forms, giving a second flush. This process can be repeated as many times as desired, provided the substrate stays contaminant free. Technically, it may be possible to achieve as many as four or five flushes from a bulk substrate before it contaminates; however, each successive flush will yield less fruit. Also, at a certain point, the advantage of pursuing additional flushes becomes negligible. The combined yield of the first, second, and third flushes is probably the most that can be milked from a single substrate. Any flushes beyond that will be small, and resources are probably better spent focusing on the next grow. However, if there is no immediate demand on time or materials, feel free to go ahead and strive for the world record in harvesting successive flushes.

6.7 GUIDE: DUNKING

To encourage the bulk substrate to produce an additional flush, we need to replenish water that the previous crop consumed. Rehydrating a bulk substrate is referred to as *dunking*, and should be carried out in a wet area. You may wish to have some old towels on hand. The easiest way to dunk a bulk substrate is to pour water directly into the monotub. The substrate will attempt to float, so it needs to be weighted to ensure it stays submerged to absorb water more effectively.

Method (see Figure 6.7)

1. Lift the monotub into the wet area. Alternatively, sit the monotub on some old towels on the floor or bench (Figure 6.7A). The substrate needs to be weighted down so that it won't float. We'll place a smaller tub on top of the substrate, and then place weights on top. Here, dumbbell plates are used (Figure 6.7B).

2. Fill the monotub with water until the substrate is fully submerged. (Figure 6.7C)

3. Leave the substrate to rehydrate for four to six hours, then remove the weights and drain off excess water (Figure 6.7D).

4. Immediately put the monotub back into fruiting conditions. Applying a fresh casing layer is optional at this point.

Figure 6.7. Dunking

A nice second flush of fruit

CHAPTER 7

Beyond the Basics

This chapter covers some intermediate/advanced methods that will allow the beginner to move beyond the basic process of growing-from-a-spore-print. Once you are comfortable with the methods discussed up to this point, and have consistently achieved good yields with low, or zero, rates of contamination, the time is right to try cloning and strain isolation.

You should also experiment with G2G transfers as a method for rapidly expanding the volume of grain spawn available for spawning to bulk. G2G transfer is a key step after cloning and strain isolation, and can also be used as a step in multispore growing.

The diagram below provides a visual representation of how these methods relate to the basic process we have learned so far of growing from a spore print.

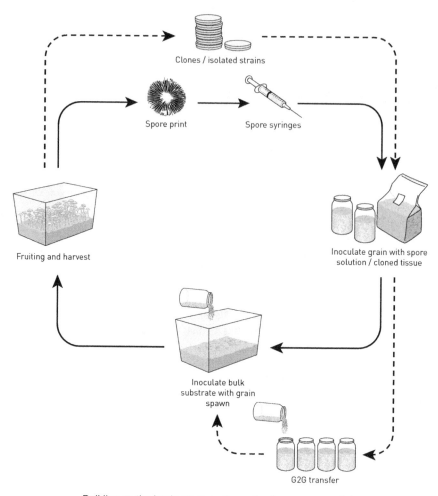

Clones / isolated strains

Spore print

Spore syringes

Fruiting and harvest

Inoculate grain with spore
solution / cloned tissue

Inoculate bulk
substrate with grain
spawn

G2G transfer

Building on the basic process of growing from a spore print

7.1 DISCUSSION: STRAIN ISOLATION AND GROWING WITH AGAR

Multispore versus Isolated Strains

Up to this point, we have focused on growing from a spore print (multispore inoculation or multispore growing). Although this method is straightforward and suitable for the beginner grower, it does come with an inherent limitation. The genetic variability contained in a spore print can lead to unpredictable performance.

A single spore print is made up of millions of spores, hence the term *multispore*. Every individual spore in a print contains a different combination of genes from its parent mushroom. For this reason, growing from a spore print will always involve a degree of uncertainty; there is no way of knowing whether the resulting mycelium will contain genes that are favorable for attaining the traits we value. In fact, successive crops originating from the same spore print may perform very differently, even when grown in identical conditions.

Clearly, this isn't ideal. If given the choice, fast-growing, high-yielding crops of highly potent fruit are always preferable. Unfortunately, we simply don't have fine enough control over these qualities when growing from a spore print.

Strain isolation allows for a greater degree of control when it comes to this natural genetic variation. Crops derived from the same isolated strain will display similar growth and fruiting characteristics, thereby allowing us to achieve a much higher level of consistency across successive crops.

Growing with Agar

Agar is a gelatinous substance used in laboratory settings for culturing microorganisms. On its own, agar has no nutritional value, so nutrients are added to make it suitable for the specific microbes being tested. Agar and nutrient powders are mixed with water, and the resulting solution is sterilized in a pressure cooker. The hot liquid agar is poured into petri dishes and allowed to cool and set, forming a flat, semisolid surface. Mushroom mycelium will grow in a radial, two-dimensional pattern across the surface of the agar from the point of inoculation, allowing for easy examination of mycelial growth. Microorganisms grown on agar in this way are referred to as *cultures*.

Working with agar has a number of benefits. Agar cultures provide a means for us to easily identify and isolate vigorous strains of *P. cubensis*. Samples of healthy, fast-growing mycelium can be transferred to fresh petri dishes, thus separating them from slower-growing and potentially less vigorous strains present in the original culture. This process is referred to as *strain isolation*.

Another advantage of working with agar is that it provides a convenient way of dealing with contamination. If a portion of an agar petri dish becomes contaminated with bacteria or mold, we can easily take a small sample of mycelium from an uncontaminated portion of the culture and transfer it to a new plate, leaving the contaminant behind. This isn't possible when using growing media such as grain or bulk substrate. If these growing media become contaminated, there is usually little that can be done to save them.

Finally, agar provides a means for long-term storage of strains that we want to keep. Mycelium stored in agar test tubes (called *slants*) and refrigerated will stay viable for many years, and can be instantly retrieved from storage when needed. Using agar as a storage medium, the grower can build up a collection of interesting strains he or she has developed over time.

Strain Isolation

Strain isolation involves inoculating agar petri dishes with spores or living tissue taken from a fruit body (*cloning*) or another culture (*subculturing*), and then choosing the most vigorous strains of mycelium for further isolation and testing. The goal is to obtain a single high-performing strain (also referred to as a *monoculture* or *isolate*) that can be used as the starting point for multiple future grows.

The easiest way to obtain a high-quality culture is to sample tissue from a fruit body, such as one collected from a multispore grow. This is referred to as cloning because the resulting culture will be genetically identical to the mushroom from which the sample was collected.

Strain isolation starting from spores requires a greater investment of time in comparison to cloning due to the fact that the initial culture contains many more individual strains that must be thinned out over repeated transfers. The eventual isolates then need to be tested on grain and bulk substrate to see if they possess favorable cropping characteristics. When growing out an isolated strain, we look for rapid growth rates when colonizing grain and bulk substrates, dense pin sets, low rates of aborts, well-formed fruit, high yield, and high potency. Once an isolated strain is tested and is proven to be a high performer, we can save the strain for future use.

Starting with spores

We can start a culture from spores by transferring spores from a spore print, or by placing a drop of spore solution onto a petri dish. Using either of these methods will result in multiple strains growing on the initial culture, and it will be impossible to identify a single strain without first making multiple transfers.

A small sample can be taken from a rapidly growing section of mycelium and transferred to a new petri dish. This process is repeated—always sampling from the healthiest mycelium that appears to be the most vigorous—until a single strain is isolated. It is likely to take at least nine or ten transfers to isolate a single strain when starting from spores.

When sampling this way, the hope is that the vigorous growth of the mycelium on agar is a predictor of vigor at later stages of growth as well. However, this remains unpredictable until the candidate strain is grown out and observed at all stages of the growing cycle.

Culturing from spores has some notable advantages. Spore prints stay viable for years and are easily stored, making them a convenient source of genetic material for culturing. Spores also have the benefit of allowing us to begin a culture afresh with a range of new genetic strains from which to choose. Old cultures that we have developed over time that have undergone many transfers and large numbers of cell divisions may experience *senescence*, a condition where the culture's ability to produce healthy mycelium and fruit bodies declines. A previously high-performing strain can become less vigorous over time due to senescence. Starting a new culture from spores allows new vigorous strains to be identified and developed.

Cloning

Cloning is probably the fastest way to get a sample of high-performing genetics for culturing. Taking a clone is as simple as identifying a prime fruit body or cluster of fruit bodies from a multispore grow and growing a tissue sample on agar. Crops originating from a clone will be genetically identical to the parent mushroom, and will be similar to the parent when it comes to traits such as growth rate, potency, and fruit size.

Cloning, therefore, is a more direct way of obtaining high-quality genetics compared to culturing from spores because the starting sample has proven growth characteristics and fruiting potential.

Cloning may result in isolation of a single strain straight away, or, more likely, multiple strains. This is because *P. cubensis* mushrooms originating from a multispore grow can either be composed of mycelium from a single strain or from several strains. Isolates made from a clone that are shown to be a composite of different strains won't necessarily perform better than the original clone. In fact, it is possible that such isolates could perform poorly compared to the original clone. The clone has demonstrated growth and fruiting characteristics, whereas an isolate taken from a composite clone will need to be grown out and tested to ensure its performance.

As well as being an ideal starting point for strain isolation, clones are also an excellent starting point for bulk grows. A clone can be used to inoculate grain, which can, in turn, be expanded via G2G transfers and eventually spawned to bulk. Crops derived from clones will usually have more predictable fruiting characteristics than multispore grows, and should display traits similar to the parent fruit body.

Performing an isolation

When performing an isolation—regardless of whether we begin with spores or a clone—our goal is to identify a single vigorous strain that can be sampled and grown in isolation on a fresh plate. When working with agar cultures, we can imagine the face of a clock overlaying the culture to describe positions of interest.

As mycelium radiates outward from the point of inoculation, differences in growth rate can be observed between neighboring strains. Differentiation between strains is referred to as *sectoring*. We look at the outer perimeter of mycelial growth, and take samples from the strongest and fastest-growing strain. This sample is then transferred to a new petri dish and allowed to grow out.

Several transfers may be required before sectoring becomes apparent, especially when beginning with spores. This is because the initial cultures will usually have multiple strains growing over the top of one another. Several transfers are made to thin out the number of strains present. In the case of a clone culture, we may see a single strain straight away, or, more likely, if the fruit was a composite of several strains, we will see sectoring in the cloned culture. It is safe to assume that there will be fewer strains present in a culture derived from a clone compared to one derived from spores. Therefore less transfers will be required to isolate a single strain from a clone than from an initial culture derived from spores.

A successfully isolated strain should show no sectoring at all. We'd expect an isolated single strain to show a uniform pattern of radial growth from the point of inoculation. After a single strain is isolated and tested for suitable cropping characteristics, it can be stored long term on agar slants.

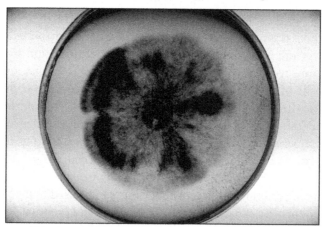

This clone taken from a fruit body clearly shows sectoring

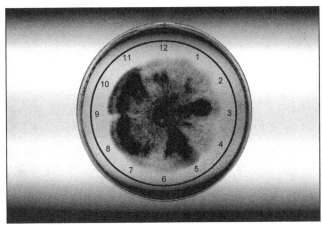

We can imagine the face of a clock overlaying the culture to describe positions of interest

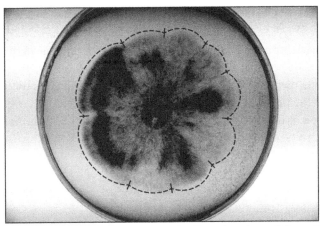

We can visually identify sectors by examining the leading edge of mycelial growth around the perimeter of the culture

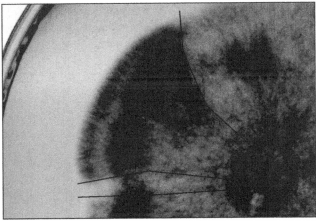

The sector between 9 and 11 o'clock shows faster growth than neighbouring sectors. Samples could be taken from this sector for the purpose of isolating a single strain

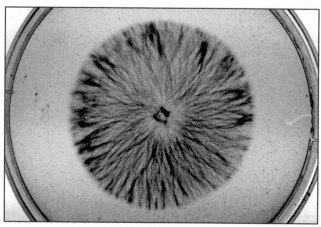

An isolated strain showing no sectoring at all

7.2 GUIDE: AGAR PREPARATION AND POURING PETRI DISHES

This method demonstrates how to prepare malt extract agar (MEA), a recipe that will provide optimal conditions for culturing *P. cubensis*.

Ingredients used in the agar recipe will be mixed in a glass bottle and then sterilized in the pressure cooker. To avoid having the agar boil over inside the pressure cooker, it is important to use a bottle that is 1.5–2 times the volume of the agar mixture we are preparing. If preparing 500 mL of agar, a 1 L bottle is ideal, whereas a 750 mL bottle will suffice.

Agar Preparation

Materials

- 1 L or 750 mL glass bottle
- Customized bottle lid
- Plastic funnel
- Agar powder
- Light malt extract powder

Recipe

- 500 mL water
- 10 g agar powder
- 10 g light malt extract

Method (see Figure 7.2.1)

1. The bottle lid needs to be customized to allow movement of air both in and out of the bottle. After sterilization, air will be drawn into the bottle as the agar cools and contracts. A filter placed into the lid or neck of the bottle prevents airborne contaminants from entering and coming into contact with the freshly sterilized agar.

Drill a hole in the lid (Figure 7.2.1A), and place a disk of compressed felt into the top of the lid to act as a filter (Figure 7.2.1B). Alternatively, a wad of synthetic cushion filler can be inserted into the neck of the bottle to act as a filter.

2. Pour the dry ingredients through a funnel into the bottle (Figure 7.2.1E).

3. Add 100 mL of water to the bottle, and then vigorously swirl the bottle until the dry ingredients have dissolved (Figure 7.2.1G). Add the remaining 400 mL of water (Figure 7.2.1H), and swirl to mix.

4. Fasten the lid to the bottle, ensuring a filter is in place as described above. Cover the lid and neck of bottle with aluminum foil. Fold the foil down the sides of the bottle (Figure 7.2.1J).

5. Load the bottle into a pressure cooker, and cook at 15 psi for thirty minutes.

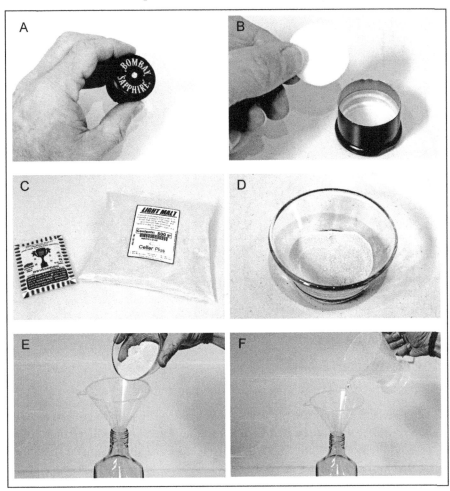

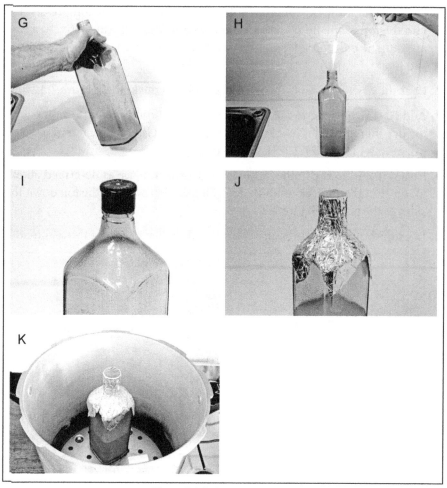

Figure 7.2.1. Agar preparation

Pouring Petri Dishes

Materials
- Petri dishes
- Sterilized MEA agar

Method (see Figure 7.2.2)

1. Prepare the sterile work area as described in chapter 2.

2. After sterilization in the pressure cooker, allow the agar to cool to a point where the bottle can be handled. Wrapping a freshly laundered tea towel around the bottle of hot agar will make it easier to hold. Transfer the bottle of agar and petri dishes to your SAB.

3. Inside the SAB, remove the foil and lid from the agar bottle. Firmly grasp the bottle in one hand in preparation to pour. With your free hand, lift the lid from a petri dish, and then pour only enough agar to cover the bottom of the plate (Figure 7.2.2D).

When lifting the lid from a petri dish, hold it by the sides and keep the underside of the lid facing directly down (Figure 7.2.2E).

Work quickly with smooth, unhurried motions. Don't allow the agar to cool too much in the bottle, or it will set.

4. Once you have finished, carefully stack the dishes and cover them with the bag in which they were originally packed (Figure 7.2.2G). Allow the petri dishes to sit for an hour and cool before use.

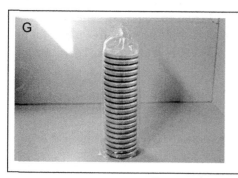

Figure 7.2.2. Pouring petri dishes

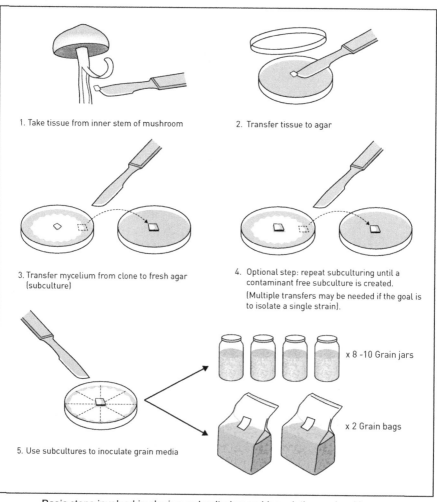

1. Take tissue from inner stem of mushroom

2. Transfer tissue to agar

3. Transfer mycelium from clone to fresh agar (subculture)

4. Optional step: repeat subculturing until a contaminant free subculture is created.
(Multiple transfers may be needed if the goal is to isolate a single strain).

x 8 -10 Grain jars

x 2 Grain bags

5. Use subcultures to inoculate grain media

Basic steps involved in cloning, subculturing and inoculating grain with agar

7.3 GUIDE: SIMPLE CLONING METHOD

Clones can be taken from mushrooms at any stage of development. Generally, the sample should be from well-formed mushrooms with an overall healthy appearance.

The cloning process is conducted inside a SAB or in front of a flow hood. Tissue samples are taken from inside the stem of the chosen mushroom and placed on petri dishes containing agar. Over the following days, mycelium will grow out radially from the tissue onto the agar. Small samples of this fresh mycelium are transferred to one or more new petri dishes, leaving behind any contaminants that may have been introduced with the initial tissue sample.

This process of agar-to-agar transfer is called subculturing. A vigorous, contaminant-free culture produced from one or more cycles of subculturing can be used to inoculate grain. Grain jars inoculated this way can be used as master jars to inoculate more grain jars/bags via G2G transfers. Alternatively, subcultures can be used to inoculate larger volumes of grain in bags, which can be spawned to bulk directly without additional G2G transfers.

In this way, clones taken from a single mushroom can be used as the basis for numerous future grows.

Materials
- Mushroom(s)
- Prepared agar dishes

Method (see Figure 7.3)

1. Prepare the sterile work area as described in chapter 2.

2. Position the petri dishes, mushrooms, and scalpel inside the SAB. Position the spirit burner outside the SAB within easy reach, and light it. Give your hands another wipe, and then begin work.

3. Inside the SAB, tear open the mushroom with your fingers to expose the tissue at the center of the stem (Figure 7.3F). Avoid cutting the stem open, because the blade of the scalpel could push contaminants on the outside of the mushroom into the inner area from which we'll be collecting tissue. Don't touch the inner portion of the mushroom stem with your fingers.

4. Flame-sterilize the scalpel blade by holding it to a flame for five seconds, or until is glows red (Figure 7.3G). Cut or scrape a small piece of tissue from the freshly exposed stem (Figure 7.3H). Transfer the tissue to a petri dish (Figure 7.3I).

   When opening a petri dish, the lid should be raised the minimum amount necessary for you to reach in with the scalpel blade and place the tissue on the agar. Refit the lid as quickly as possible. Work with smooth, unhurried motions.

5. Repeat the process to create as many clones as desired. Flame-sterilize the scalpel blade before making each clone.

6. Label each plate with the date and identifying information (Figure 7.3J). Store at room temperature. Allow around two to three weeks for cultures to grow.

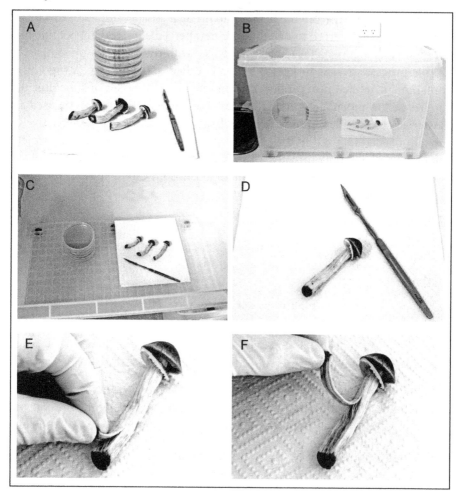

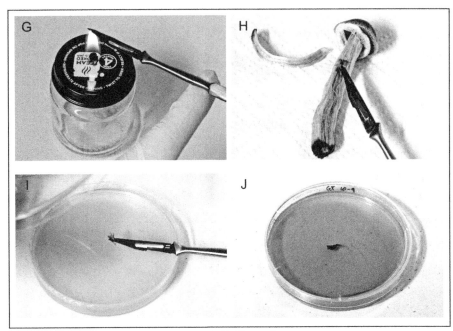

Figure 7.3. Making a clone

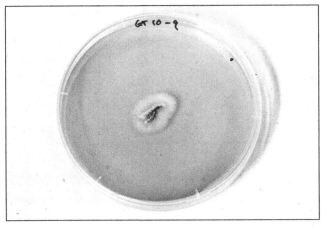

Mycelium growing outward in a radial pattern from cloned mushroom tissue

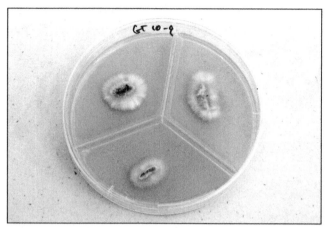

Sectioned petri dishes allow multiple clones to be grown on a single plate

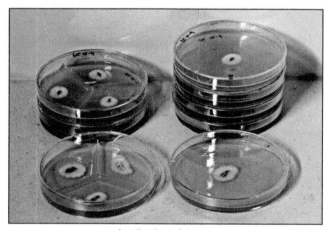

A collection of clones

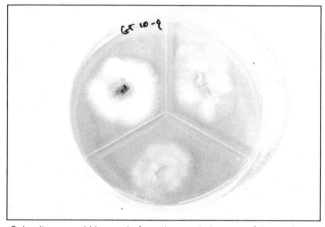

Subcultures could be made from the most vigorous of these clones

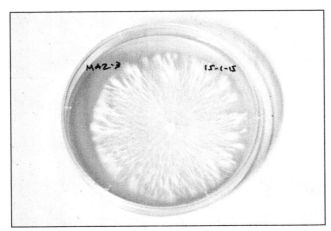

A vigorous clone culture

7.4 GUIDE: SIMPLE SUBCULTURING METHOD

Subculturing is the process of taking a small sample from an agar culture and moving it to a fresh plate. We may create subcultures to move our isolated mycelium away from contaminants on the originating plate, or as a step in the process of strain isolation.

Method (see Figure 7.4)

1. Prepare the sterile work area as described in chapter 2.

2. Flame-sterilize your scalpel blade.

3. Inside your SAB, lift the lid of the original culture plate, and use the scalpel to cut a small cube of agar and mycelium (Figure 7.4B). Choose a location on the leading edge of mycelial growth radiating out from the original tissue sample.

4. Skewer the cube of agar with the scalpel (Figure 7.4C), and transfer it to a new petri dish (Figure 7.4D). Place the cube of agar face down onto the new petri dish, sandwiching the mycelium between the cube and surface of the new agar plate.

Repeat the process to create as many subcultures as desired. Store at room temperature.

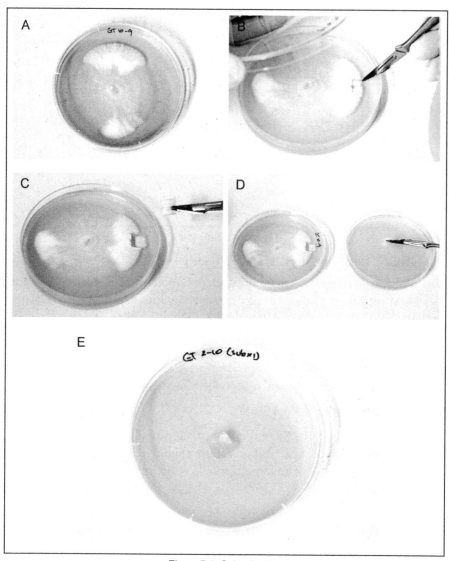

Figure 7.4. Subculturing

7.5 DISCUSSION: CONTAMINATION ON AGAR

Contamination can be a problem when working with agar because mold and bacteria can thrive on the agar medium. Transferring samples of mycelium to new plates allows us to leave behind any contaminants, thus achieving contaminant-free cultures. When transferring samples to new petri dishes, it is important to select only contaminant-free mycelium. Hyphae will always grow in a radial pattern outward from the original piece of tissue. Contaminants can take the form of anything other than this radial growth of hyphae. Small satellite colonies surrounding the transferred tissue are a clear indication of contamination. In practice, it may take more than one transfer to achieve a completely contaminant-free culture.

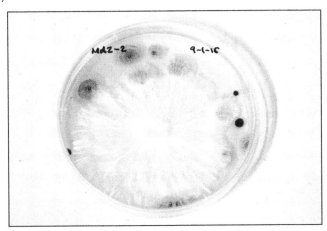

Mold contaminants growing on a culture

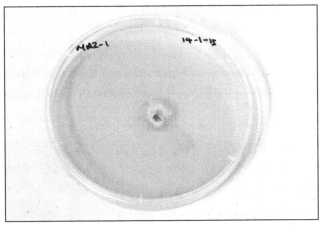

Bacterial contamination surrounding a cloned tissue sample

7.6 GUIDE: AGAR-TO-GRAIN TRANSFERS

Once we have a vigorous, contaminant-free culture of mycelium growing on agar, we can use it to inoculate grain medium, which, in turn, can be used to inoculate greater volumes of grain medium. In this way, a single culture can be expanded to produce enough grain spawn for use in a bulk grow. Agar-to-grain transfers are conducted inside the SAB. Usually, a single culture is used to inoculate six to eight grain jars, which are then used as master jars for G2G transfers. It is also possible to transfer agar to grain medium in spawn bags, thus allowing for inoculation of a larger volume of grain in the first step.

Materials
- Agar culture(s)
- Sterilized grain jars

Method (see Figure 7.6)

1. Prepare the sterile work area as described in chapter 2.

2. Clean the recipient jars by wiping them all over with a paper towel soaked in 70 percent isopropanol. Pay close attention to the underside of the lid rim.

3. Position the agar cultures, grain jars, and scalpel inside the SAB. Position the spirit burner outside the SAB within easy reach, and light it. Give your hands another wipe, and then begin work.

4. Loosen the lid of each recipient jar, but don't remove the lids at this stage.

5. Flame-sterilize the scalpel. Inside the SAB, use your free hand to lift the lid of a culture and set it aside. Use the scalpel to slice the agar plate into six to eight equally sized portions (Figure 7.6D).

6. Transfer a portion of agar and mycelium to each recipient jar (Figure 7.6E). As you work, don't allow your arm to hover over the culture or the open mouth of the recipient grain jar. It is good practice to avoid touching the scalpel blade against anything other than the agar. Don't set the scalpel down or touch it against the neck of the recipient jar.

7. Incubate grain jars at room temperature. Once they are fully colonized, use the grain jars as master jars for further inoculations via G2G transfer.

Figure 7.6. Agar-to-grain transfer

Agar to spawn bag transfers

Agar can also be used to inoculate grain in spawn bags rather than jars. In this way, a larger volume of grain can be inoculated in the first agar-to-grain transfer. Colonized spawn bags can then be spawned to bulk. Inoculate one bag at a time inside the SAB. See page 127 for a detailed description of inoculating spawn bags in the confines of a SAB.

7.7 DISCUSSION: GRAIN-TO-GRAIN TRANSFERS

G2G transfer is a useful technique for rapidly inoculating large amounts of grain, thereby expanding the quantity of spawn available for bulk grows. Grain inoculated via G2G transfers will colonize more quickly than grain inoculated with spore solution. The process involves transferring small quantities of spawn from a fully colonized master jar into sterilized grain jars or bags. A single master jar can be used to inoculate up to ten grain jars or an equivalent amount of grain in bags.

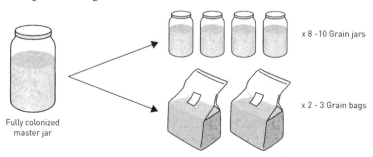

Fully colonized master jar → x 8 -10 Grain jars / x 2 - 3 Grain bags

G2G transfers are a key step after cloning and strain isolation. Once an agar culture has been used to inoculate a grain jar, that jar can be treated as a master jar for G2G transfers. In this way, the volume of cultured mycelium is expanded to a quantity sufficient for use in a bulk grow.

G2G transfers can also be used as a step in multispore growing, simply to expand the volume of grain available for spawning to bulk. This is extremely useful if you are working with multiple monotubs.

G2G transfers should always be performed inside a SAB or in front of a flow hood. Jars can be loaded into the SAB in batches. Spawn bags, however, can be challenging to handle in the confined space of a SAB. Spawn bags are quite tall when unfolded, and the average SAB usually doesn't have enough vertical space to tip spawn comfortably into an opened bag from above. It's possible to get around this by laying the spawn bag on its side. This arrangement necessitates loading only one bag into the SAB at a time.

7.8 GUIDE: GRAIN-TO-GRAIN TRANSFERS

Materials
- Master grain jar
- Recipient grain jars or grain spawn bags

Method—Canning Jars (see Figure 7.8.1)

1. Prepare the sterile work area as described in chapter 2.

2. Break up the colonized grain inside the master jar by knocking it against a firm-but-yielding surface, such as an exercise foam roller, the arm of a couch, or a phone book (Figure 7.8.1B). The grain should be thoroughly broken up so that it can easily be tipped in handful-sized quantities into the recipient jars (Figure 7.8.1C).

3. Thoroughly clean the master jar by wiping it all over with a paper towel soaked in 70 percent isopropanol (Figure 7.8.1D). Pay close attention to the underside of the lid rim. Place the master jar inside the SAB.

4. A good way to conduct G2G transfers is to sterilize the recipient jars or bags immediately before conducting the G2G transfer. Once the recipient grain vessels have cooled, you can move them straight from the sterile interior of the pressure cooker to the SAB, no cleaning necessary.

   If the recipient jars/bags were temporarily stored after sterilization, they should be cleaned before the grain transfer is performed. Thoroughly wipe recipient jars all over, again paying extra care to wipe up under the rim of the lid.

5. Load as many grain jars into the SAB as will comfortably fit while allowing adequate space to work.

6. Inside the SAB, loosen the lid on each recipient jar and the master jar.

7. Remove the lid from the master jar and set it aside. Lift the lid of a recipient jar, and then quickly tip or shake a handful of grain spawn from the master jar into the recipient jar (Figure 7.8.1H). Quickly refit the lid to the recipient jar.

   Try to have the lid of the recipient jar lifted for no more than a few seconds. Avoid touching the lip of the master jar against recipient jars while dispensing colonized grain. Perform the grain transfer using smooth, unhurried motions. Avoid abrupt, rapid movements that could generate air currents. Repeat the process to transfer a handful of grain spawn into each recipient jar.

8. Refit the lid to the master jar, and set the jar aside. Screw the lids down firmly on each of the recipient jars, and then remove the jars from the SAB.

9. Load the next batch of recipient jars into the SAB, and repeat the process.

10. Give each recipient jar a shake to disperse the spawn. Label the jars, and allow them to colonize.

Figure 7.8.1. Grain-to-grain transfers - canning jars

Method—Spawn Bags (see Figure 7.8.2)

The process is essentially the same, but with some slight adaptations to allow for the unwieldy nature of grain bags.

1. Thoroughly clean the master jar, and break up the colonized grain as described above. Place the master jar inside the SAB.

2. Load a single grain bag into the SAB. Unfold the flap, and lay the bag on its side as shown (Figure 7.8.2D). If transferring the bag straight from the pressure cooker, no cleaning is required. Otherwise, wipe the top portion of the bag with a paper towel soaked in 70 percent isopropanol.

3. Loosen the lid of the master jar, but don't remove the lid at this point.

4. Open the bag in preparation to receive colonized grain spawn. Grip the opposite sides of the neck of the bag in your fingertips, and carefully pull to open the bag (Figure 7.8.2E). Don't touch the opening of the bag with your fingers.

5. Hold the bag open as shown. With your free hand, remove the lid from the master jar and put it aside. Tip, or shake, between one-third and one-half of the master jar's contents into the recipient grain bag (Figure 7.8.2F).

   Quickly refit the lid to the master jar, and put the jar aside. Lift and fold the neck of the bag to allow the colonized grain to slide down inside (Figure 7.8.2G).

6. Seal the bag with a Ziploc tie (Figure 7.8.2H).

7. Repeat the process for as many grain bags as required, remembering to wipe your hands each time, and to clean the bags as necessary.

8. Knead the grain through the bag to disperse the spawn throughout (Figure 7.8.2I). Label the bags, and allow them to colonize.

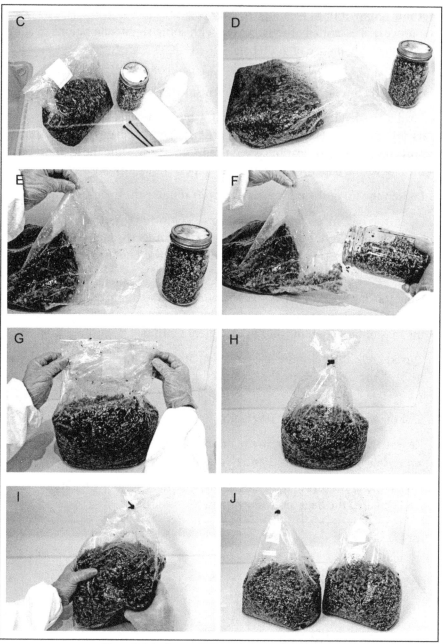

Figure 7.8.2. Grain-to-grain transfers - spawn bags

7.9 GUIDE: MAKING AGAR SLANTS

Once we have identified a high-performing strain or clone, we may want to keep it for future use. Test tubes are useful for long-term storage of cultures. Agar stored in test tubes is less likely to dry out over long periods due to tight-fitting lids and a reduced surface area of agar exposed to air. By comparison, petri dishes are designed for short-term testing and culturing, and aren't suitable for long-term storage of cultures.

Agar slants are prepared by filling test tubes halfway with agar and allowing them to cool at an angle, creating a larger surface area for the culture to colonize than there would be if they were allowed to set standing upright. By adding a small piece of wood to each test tube for the mycelium to colonize, we can increase the time that cultures will remain viable in storage. We could expect cultures prepared this way to remain healthy for up to five years before transferring to fresh slants would become necessary.

By storing our best strains and clones this way, we are able to build up a library of high-performing genetics we can use in the future. Beginning a fresh culture from an agar slant is simply a matter of taking a small sample from a slant and transferring it to a petri dish. Once that dish has colonized sufficiently, it can be used to inoculate grain.

Preparing Agar Slants

Materials
- Culture test tubes (e.g., 17 mm × 100 mm)
- Test tube holder rack
- MEA
- Syringe
- Wide mouth jar
- Wooden sticks (e.g., skewers, popsicle sticks)

Method (see Figure 7.9.1)

1. Break the wooden sticks into 6–7 cm (2.5 in) sections (Figure 7.9.1A). Drop them into a pot of heated water, and allow them to soak for one hour (Figure 7.9.1B).

2. After soaking, drop a section of stick into each test tube (Figure 7.9.1C).

3. Prepare the agar using the MEA recipe described in this book. Weigh the dry ingredients (Figure 7.9.1D). Use boiling water to mix the solution; this will help dissolve the agar and malt extract into solution. The agar will be sterilized in the pressure cooker after being poured into the test tubes.

4. Using a syringe, carefully fill each test tube with 7 mL of MEA (Figure 7.9.1E), and loosely apply the lids.

5. Stand the test tubes in a wide-mouthed jar. Fill the jar with water so that the test tubes are halfway submerged (Figure 7.9.1F), then cover the jar with a piece of foil. Adding water to the jar moderates the heating and cooling of the agar while in the pressure cooker, and helps prevent agar boiling over.

6. Sterilize the agar test tubes in the pressure cooker at 15 psi for thirty minutes.

7. After sterilization is complete, remove the jar containing the test tubes from the pressure cooker and transfer it to your sterile SAB work area.

8. Place the test tubes into the test tube holder rack. Tilt the rack at roughly a 45-degree angle, and leave the agar to set (Figure 7.9.1H).

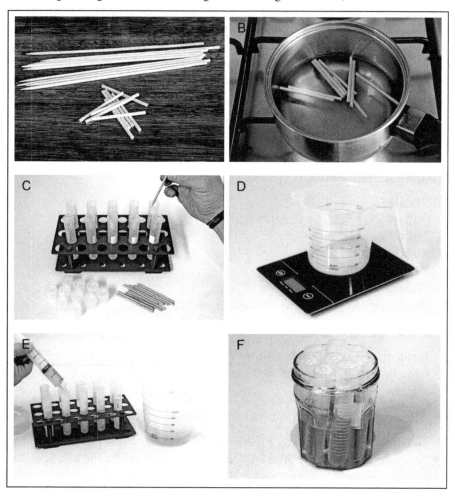

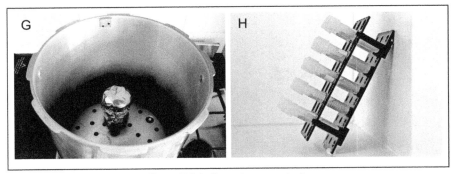

Figure 7.9.1. Preparing agar slants

Inoculating Agar Slants

Materials
- Prepared agar slant test tubes
- Healthy culture
- Thin metal implement (e.g., scalpel, inoculation loop)

Method (see Figure 7.9.2)

1. Prepare the sterile work area as described in chapter 2. Thoroughly sterilize the metal implement. Wipe its length with a paper towel soaked in 70 percent isopropanol, and flame-sterilize the tip.

2. Loosen the cap of a recipient agar slant. Take a sample of mycelium from the leading edge of the donor culture (Figure 7.9.2B). Lift the lid from the recipient slant, and place the sampled tissue onto the agar surface (Figure 7.9.2C). Be careful not to touch the metal implement against the inner sides of the recipient test tube. Snap the test tube lid down tightly.

3. Label the agar slants appropriately (Figure 7.9.2D), and leave them for several days to colonize at room temperature. Once the culture is established and mycelium can be seen growing on the agar surface, bag the agar slants (Figure 7.9.2E) and transfer them to a refrigerator for long-term storage.

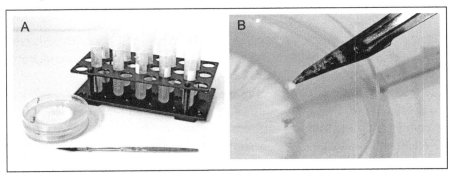

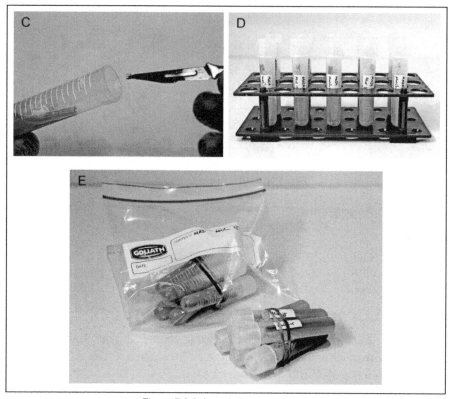

Figure 7.9.2. Inoculating agar slants

7.10 DISCUSSION: HEPA-FILTER FLOW HOOD

A flow hood can be used interchangeably with a SAB to perform sterile procedures. This book advocates starting out with a SAB because it is low cost and provides reliable protection against airborne contaminants, making it perfect for the beginner grower on a budget. By now, however, you will have discovered for yourself that the trusty SAB has some limitations when it comes to space. This is where a flow hood has the edge. It provides a more open and comfortable space to work in.

A flow hood works by blowing a steady stream of air through a specialized filter called a *high-efficiency particulate air* (HEPA) filter. The area immediately downstream of the HEPA filter is effectively cleaned of airborne contaminants, providing us with a sterile space to work in.

The airflow delivered to the work space is described as a *laminar flow*, which means that the airflow is streamlined, nonturbulent, and free of fluctuations or eddies that could lead to a mix of filtered and unfiltered air.

Whether you decide to buy a commercially produced flow hood or buy the materials and assemble one yourself, a flow hood is rather expensive.

Commercially available flow hoods cost anywhere from five hundred dollars up to many thousands, depending on size and type. Making one yourself will reduce the cost considerably, but you should still expect to pay between two and three hundred dollars, with the HEPA filter and the blower accounting for much of that cost. In addition, sourcing an appropriate HEPA filter and a blower to match can be a challenge (see chapter 8 for sourcing suggestions).

Working with a Flow Hood

Before using the flow hood to conduct sterile procedures, allow it to run for thirty to forty-five minutes to blow off any dust particles that may have settled on the outside of the filter. The bench and equipment should also be thoroughly wiped clean with a paper towel soaked in 70 percent isopropanol.

Equipment should be placed close to the filter. The most sterile area is next to the filter where airflow is strongest. Sterility declines the further away you are from the flow hood.

Always place the cleanest equipment and materials upstream of dirtier items. For example, if you were about to conduct a series of G2G transfers, a master jar that has been colonizing on a shelf and exposed to the open air would be considered less clean than sterilized recipient grain jars that have come straight from the pressure cooker. Of course, the master jar is wiped clean before being placed into the sterile area, but it would nevertheless be considered the dirtier item when it comes to this particular example and would therefore be placed downstream of the recipient jars.

Similarly, keep your gloved hands downstream of sterile equipment and materials. Despite our best efforts, our hands always have a greater risk of carrying contaminants because they are constantly touching items.

The spirit burner is placed within easy reach to the side of the flow hood and out of the direct air flow.

Preparing to do agar work in front of the flow hood

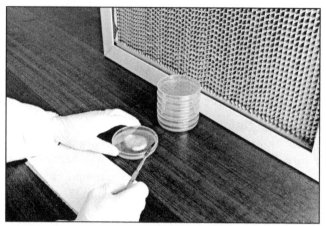

Performing a subculture in front of the flow hood. Fresh petri dishes are placed upstream.

7.11 GUIDE: CONSTRUCTING A HEPA-FILTER FLOW HOOD—CALCULATIONS

When building a flow hood, you should choose a HEPA filter first and then choose a blower to suit the specifications of the filter. The HEPA filter must be rated at 99.97–99.99 percent efficiency at 0.3 μm. This means that the filter can remove airborne particles down to the size of 0.3 μm with 99.97–99.99 percent efficiency.

The filter should be wide and tall enough to allow adequate space for conducting sterile procedures, such as G2G transfers and agar work.

Take note of the filter's airflow and resistance characteristics recorded on the data sheet. Pay attention to values such as nominal airflow capacity, initial pressure drop, and/or static pressure. This information tells us about the filter's resistance to airflow at recommended nominal airflow rates. In general terms, we need a HEPA filter with low-airflow and high-resistance characteristics. For example, air flow for a suitable HEPA filter could be in the order of about 550–1,000 m3/h (320–600 cfm), depending on the filter's surface area, whereas resistance should be 200–250 Pa (0.8–1 iwc).

Matching a blower to the HEPA filter

The following example demonstrates how to match a blower to a HEPA filter. A number of steps are involved, and the process is further complicated by the fact that manufacturers of both filters and blowers use interchangeable measurements to record airflow and pressure specifications. Some basic conversion information is provided below. Unit conversion charts are provided in chapter 8.

HEPA filter and a centrifugal blower

Airflow is usually recorded as either cubic meters per hour (m3/h) or cubic feet per minute (cfm):

1 m3/h = 0.588 cfm
1 cfm = 1.699 m3/h

Pressure values are usually recorded in pascals (Pa) or inch water column (iwc). Note that inch water column is equivalent to inch water gauge (iwg):

250 Pa = 1 iwc

Calculating the blower's required airflow

The HEPA filter's data sheet provides us the following details:

- Physical size: 64 cm wide × 32 cm high × 15 cm deep

- Rated airflow capacity: 600 m3/h (353 cfm) @ 220 Pa (0.88 iwc)

The airflow capacity rating tells us that when the filter is operated at 100 percent airflow capacity (600 m3/h or 353 cfm), the static pressure at the surface of the filter is 220 Pa (0.88 iwc).

The required airspeed in the work area is 0.5 m/s (meters per second), which is equal to 100 fpm (feet per minute). This is a known value that we specify, and we can base our calculations on achieving this airspeed.

Knowing the physical dimensions of the filter and the desired airspeed in the work space, we are able to calculate the required airflow to be delivered by the blower:

filter width (m) × filter height (m) × work space airspeed (m/s)
$0.32 \times 0.64 \times 0.5 = 0.1204$ m3/s

Multiply this value by 60 and then 60 again to convert from cubic meters per second (m3/s) to cubic meters per minute (m3/m) and then cubic meters per hour (m3/h):

0.1204 m3/s $\times 60 \times 60 = 369$ m3/h

This value can be converted to cubic feet per minute (cfm):

$369 \times 0.588 = 217$ cfm

Therefore, we need a blower that can deliver 369 m3/h (217 cfm) at a static pressure of 220 Pa (0.88 iwc). Using industry language, we'd say the blower needs to operate at the "duty point" 369 m3/h (217 cfm) at a pressure of 220 Pa (0.88 iwc).

At this point, it would be possible to purchase a blower by using the specifications calculated above. However, we should first consider whether to include a prefilter in our flow hood. Although a prefilter isn't essential, it can significantly increase the usable life expectancy of the HEPA filter and is recommended.

Prefilters

A prefilter can be used to remove coarse particles (e.g., hair and dust) from the air before delivering airflow to the HEPA filter. A prefilter can significantly prolong the life of the HEPA filter by preventing it from prematurely clogging up with dust. As a rule of thumb, a HEPA filter should be changed when it has accumulated 1.3–1.8 kg (3–4 lb) of dust load per 1,000 cfm of capacity.

The prefilter should always be positioned at an air intake upstream of the blower. Never position it between the blower and the HEPA filter, because this can reduce the pressure at the surface of the HEPA, which can, in turn, result in a less effective laminar airflow downstream of the HEPA. Therefore, including a prefilter in the flow hood requires construction of a separate chamber for the blower, with a prefilter installed at the chamber's intake.

The resistance added to the system by the prefilter needs to be worked into our calculations when estimating the required blower airflow. Prefilter material typically exerts a resistance around 37–55 Pa (0.15–0.22 iwc). If in doubt, assume resistance is 50 Pa (0.2 iwc).

Using our HEPA-filter specifications from above combined with a prefilter with a resistance of 50 Pa (0.2 iwc), we can conclude we'll need a blower capable of delivering an airflow of 369 m3/h (217 cfm) at a pressure of 270 Pa (i.e., 220 + 50 Pa). This modification may therefore influence our choice of blower (i.e., a slightly more powerful blower is required to achieve the same airflow).

Choosing a suitable blower

In this example, we'll use a centrifugal blower, also referred to as a squirrel blower. When selecting a blower, the level of performance is indicated by volumetric airflow capacity at varying pressures. This information will usually be presented as a graph or table in the blower's data sheet.

The graph below plots the performance curves of two blowers. We know our blower needs to deliver 369 m3/h (217 cfm) at 270 Pa (1.08 iwc). A horizontal line corresponding to 270 Pa is drawn across the graph. At the point at which the line intersects each blower's performance curve, take note of the air-volume reading at the bottom of the graph.

We can see that blower A is only capable of delivering around 300 m3/h (176 cfm) at 270 Pa. Blower A, therefore, is underpowered for our purposes. Blower B, on the other hand, can deliver 390 m3/h (229 cfm) at 270 Pa, which is an approximately 5–6 percent greater airflow than we need.

We can now estimate the generated airspeed from blower B by dividing blower B's airflow at 270 Pa by the HEPA filter's surface area.

Convert the blower's airflow at 270 Pa from cubic meters per hour to cubic meters per second:

390 m3/h / 60 / 60 = 0.1083 m3/s

Now, divide the airflow by the filter's surface area:

0.1083 / (0.32 m × 0.64 m)
= 0.1083 / 0.2048
= 0.53 m/s

Therefore, blower B will produce airspeed of 0.53 m/s in the work space, which is very close to our target airspeed of 0.5 m/s. Given this information, blower B would be a close match for our HEPA filter.

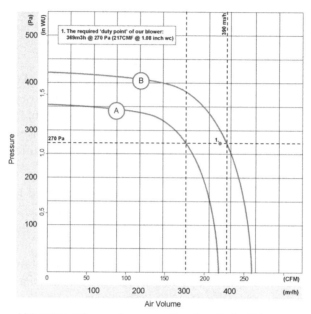

Volumetric airflow performance of two hypothetical blowers

Note that it is better to choose a slightly overpowered blower than an underpowered one, because there may be inefficiencies in the system that result in slightly less airflow delivered to the HEPA filter than our calculations might have indicated. In addition, particle buildup on the HEPA can cause increased resistance over time. With that in mind, choosing a slightly overpowered blower helps account for this variation. As a rule of thumb, it is safe to choose a blower capable of delivering up to 15 percent greater airflow than our estimated requirement. In this example, that would give leeway to choose a blower capable of delivering up to about 424 m3/h (249 cfm).

Additional considerations when choosing a blower

The guide provided here focuses on a centrifugal blower as the source of airflow; however, it is also possible to use an inline fan of the type commonly used in horticultural settings.

Blowers and fans may come with speed controllers. Although not essential, a speed controller can be a useful feature because it gives some leeway to optimize the airflow up or down.

7.12 GUIDE: CONSTRUCTING A HEPA-FILTER FLOW HOOD— ASSEMBLY

This guide demonstrates how to build a flow hood using the HEPA filter and centrifugal blower from the previous example. The body of the flow hood can be built from plywood, particle board, medium-density fiber board, or timber. In this example, white melamine particle board is used.

Materials (flow hood)

- Housing panels: (2 × sides) (2 × base and top) (1 × rear)
- 18 mm × 18 mm (0.7 in × 0.7 in) strip (for the flange)
- Trims or molding (for the front of the housing)
- Small cabinet feet (for the base of the flow hood)
- Wood screws
- Wood glue
- Silicone
- HEPA filter
- Blower

Materials (blower compartment)

- Blower compartment panels (2 × sides) (2 × front and rear panels) (1 × top panel)
- Fixed grill wall/eve vent
- Wood screws
- 4 × brackets
- Prefilter material

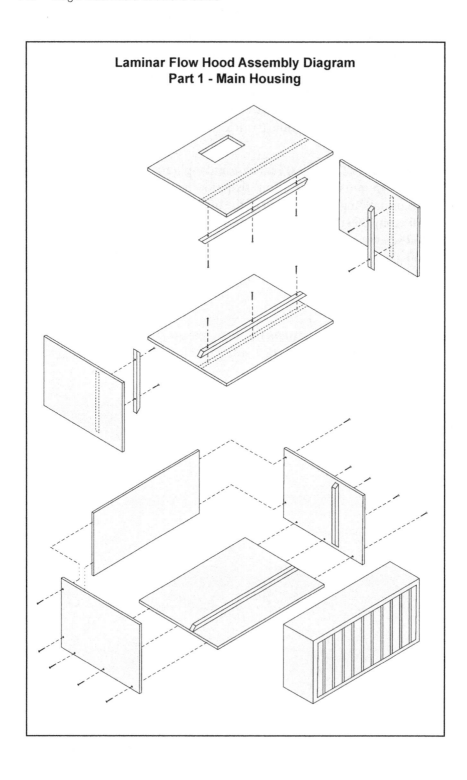

**Laminar Flow Hood Assembly Diagram
Part 1 - Main Housing**

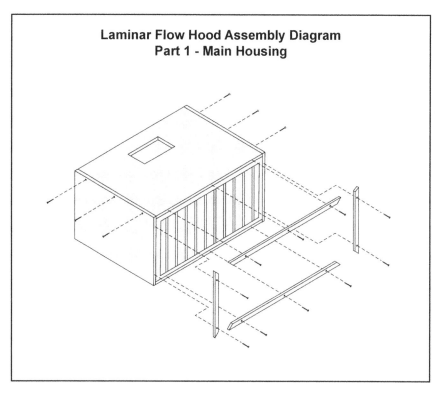

**Laminar Flow Hood Assembly Diagram
Part 1 - Main Housing**

Method (flow hood) (see Figure 7.12.1)

1. Assemble and prepare all materials first. The dimensions of the HEPA filter will determine the measurements for all housing materials.

   Cut the housing panels and wooden flange strips to size (Figure 7.12.1B). Drill pilot holes (Figure 7.12.1C). Cut a section from the top panel to match the blower outlet (Figure 7.12.1F).

2. Attach the flange pieces to the sides, base, and top housing panels (Figure 7.12.1I). The depth of the flange must match the HEPA filter's depth to allow the front of the filter to sit flush with the housing.

3. Assemble the housing. Screw the sides to the base (Figure 7.12.1J), and then install the rear panel (Figure 7.12.1K). The rear panel sits on top of the base panel. Apply wood glue to each joint before screwing in place.

4. Flip the housing over and attach the feet to the base (Figure 7.12.1L).

5. Apply silicon to the joints in the rear half of the housing (Figure 7.12.1N). Also apply silicon around the upstream joints of the flange.

   Don't apply silicon to joints downstream of the flange (i.e., the portion of the housing that will seat the HEPA filter). Use your finger to smooth the silicon into each joint (Figure 7.12.1O).

6. Prepare a gasket for the blower outlet (Figure 7.12.1Q). Placing a gasket between the blower and the top panel will help reduce any vibration. In this case, a gasket is prepared from a sheet of compressed felt.

7. Screw the blower to the top panel (Figure 7.12.1R).

8. Seat the HEPA filter into the housing, ensuring it presses firmly against the flange (Figure 7.12.1S).

9. Screw the top panel into place (Figure 7.12.1U).

10. Attach the molding or trim around the face of the housing to hold the HEPA filter tightly in place against the flange (Figure 7.12.1V).

At this point, we have built a flow hood that can be used with no further modifications. If you wish to build a compartment for the blower with a prefilter intake, continue with the following steps.

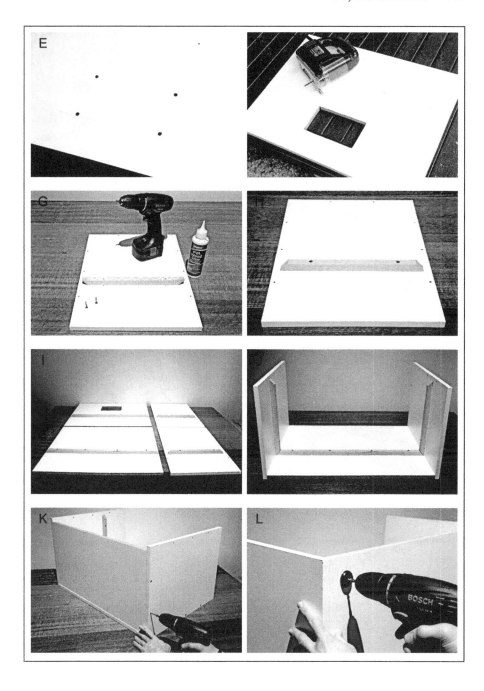

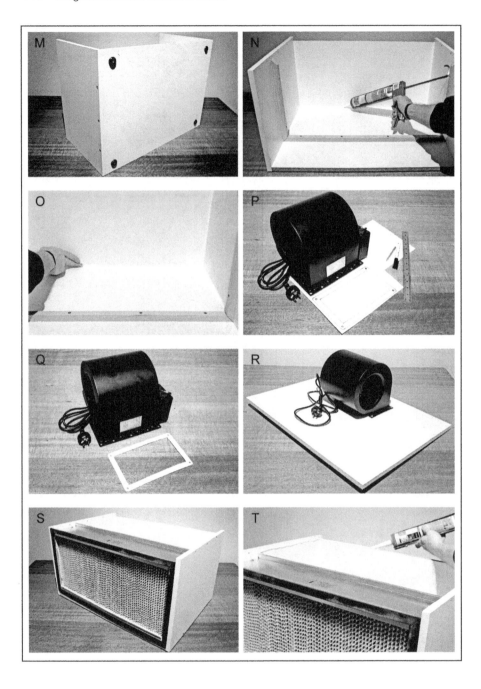

Figure 7.12.1. Constructing a HEPA-filter flow hood

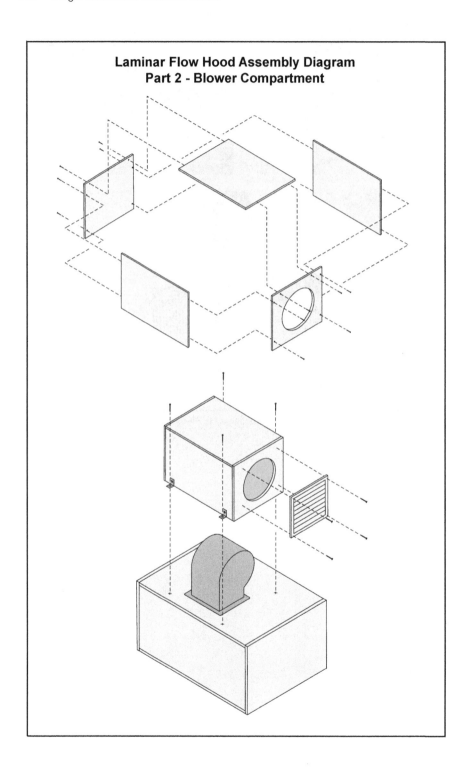

Laminar Flow Hood Assembly Diagram
Part 2 - Blower Compartment

Method (blower compartment) (see Figure 7.12.2)

1. Once again, begin by assembling and preparing all materials (Figure 7.12.2A). Cut materials to size, drill pilot holes, and remove a section from a side or rear panel to allow air intake (Figure 7.12.2C). Also remove a small arch from the rear panel to allow for the blower's power cable (Figure 7.12.2G).

   In this example, a fixed grill wall/eve vent is used as the air-intake vent for the blower compartment. The grill is detachable and allows for a piece of mesh or filter material to be fitted into the grill housing.

2. Screw the vent onto the side or rear panel (Figure 7.12.2D). Insert a section of prefilter material into the vent (Figure 7.12.2E), and then fix the vent grill into place.

3. Assemble the compartment. Screw the front panel to the sides, and then do the same for the top and rear panels. Apply wood glue to each joint.

4. Fix the compartment to the top panel of the flow hood with brackets (Figure 7.12.2K). Don't use wood glue in completing this step. We want the compartment to be easily removable to allow access to the blower, if required later on.

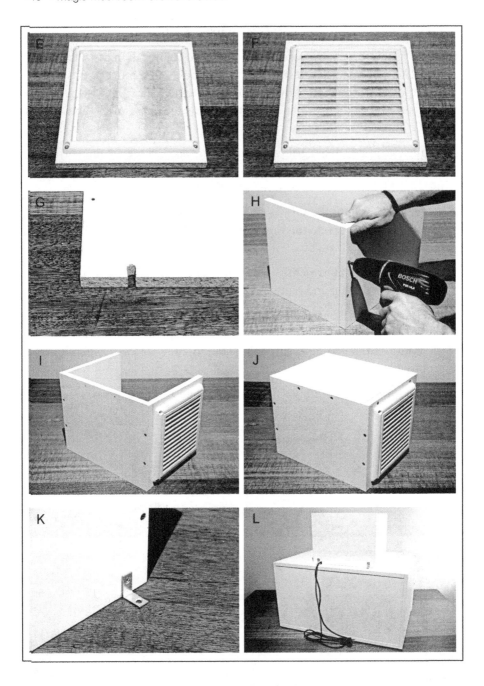

Figure 7.12.2. Constructing a HEPA-filter flow hood - blower compartment

CHAPTER 8

Additional Resources

This chapter collects together some useful resources, such as advice for sourcing materials and equipment, unit conversion charts, a timeline infographic, and links to further online resources.

8.1 DISCUSSION: SOURCING MATERIALS AND EQUIPMENT

Mushroom cultivation requires a variety of materials and equipment. Many of the items needed for grow projects can be found locally. However, some niche items may require a little detective work to track down. This section discusses places to find general supplies as well as sources for specific niche items.

General Supplies and Useful Places to Shop

Brewing Supply Stores

Brewing supply stores stock materials and equipment for home-brewing projects. Light malt extract powder, used to prepare MEA for culturing, can be found here. They might also stock useful glassware, such as autoclavable 1 L bottles (useful for pressure cooking agar), and small beakers.

Hardware Stores

Many of the essential supplies for making cultivation equipment, including the tools needed for customizations, will come from hardware stores. Plastic tubs, painter's buckets, bulk substrate ingredients, sheets of plastic for lining your monotub—all these items, to name just a few, can be sourced at your typical hardware store. In most cases, key tools, such as your drill and hole cutters or circle cutter, will also be available here. For most of your general supplies, hardware stores will be the first port of call.

Haberdashery or Craft Stores

Haberdashery or craft stores carry supplies for sewing and arts-and-crafts projects. You should be able to find sheets of compressed felt and bags of synthetic cushion filler here.

Hydroponics Shops

Hydroponics shops are good places to buy vermiculite in bulk, and possibly coconut fiber (coir) bricks as well. Although vermiculite can usually be found at gardening or hardware stores, it's usually more expensive at these places and sold in smaller bags. Hydroponics shops will often have large 100 L bags of vermiculite that are economically priced, and will provide you with enough material to last for years. Hydroponics shops will also stock seedling-propagation mats, which can be used to warm grain spawn.

Nurseries, Gardening Stores, or Agricultural Supply Stores

You should be able to find some or all of your bulk substrate ingredients here, such as coconut fiber (coir), gypsum, straw, vermiculite, and manure. Agricultural supply stores that carry equipment for livestock farming will usually stock empty syringes, which can be used for making spore syringes.

Mushroom Cultivation Specialists

As you would expect, specialist mushroom cultivation outlets carry pretty much everything you will ever need for the growing process. These places are usually online stores as opposed to brick-and-mortar shops. Many of the more specialized, niche items we need can be found here, including lab equipment, agar supplies, synthetic filter discs, and spawn bags. Mushroom cultivation specialists are also some of the only places where you can purchase *P. cubensis* spore prints.

Note that these places may not always represent the best value. For example, it is usually more economical to buy substrate ingredients separately, and then prepare them yourself, as opposed to buying pre-prepared bags from a store that specializes in mushroom cultivation.

Online Markets

Online markets are excellent sources for pretty much the whole range of equipment and materials you need. Any item that is suitable for delivery via the postal system can be bought from online markets.

Examples of items you might source from online markets include digital scales for weighing yields, empty syringes, silica gel packs, a wire-mesh strainer, a food dehydrator, all items needed for agar work and maintaining a clean work area (e.g., agar powder, petri dishes, scalpels, glassware, gloves, isopropanol, isopropanol dispenser bottles, and Tyvek sleeves), and even bulky items, such as a pressure cooker.

Scientific Equipment Wholesalers/Distributors

These enterprises aren't always open to doing business with the hobbyist or individual. Often, they are only interested in providing their products in bulk quantities to industry or other large enterprises, such as universities. Nevertheless, it's still worth contacting a few of these places on the off chance you might find a friendly operator who doesn't mind helping out. Some time ago, I had an incredibly lucky break when I called such a wholesaler in search of well-priced petri dishes. Initially, the phone contact told me the company normally sold them by the pallet load (i.e., by the tens of thousand) only. After further conversation, however, he conceded that he had a couple of spare boxes of petri dishes left over from a recent large order, and that for fifty dollars, I was welcome to one of those if I was prepared to pick it up. A box of five hundred petri dishes for fifty dollars brought the price down to ten cents per unit. I have since obtained glassware, various laboratory disposables, and other useful items for wholesale prices from the same helpful guy.

I recount this story to encourage you to get creative when searching for materials and equipment. Don't be afraid to call around and ask for help. It's amazing how far a friendly and confident demeanor can take you.

Niche Items

Acrylic

Customizing the lid of your SAB with a sheet of transparent acrylic allows for better visibility into the interior of the SAB.

The simplest way to obtain a piece of acrylic is from a specialist store. Look online for a specialist acrylic business that caters to people wanting customized sizes for use as windows or for making aquariums. With a little searching, you should be able to find a business that will cut acrylic to specification and then send it to you. Also, these places are likely to offer the best prices since they regularly deal with high volumes.

Alternatively, you can buy precut acrylic from a hardware store, but it's likely to be more expensive. With luck, you might find a precut sheet that fits the lid of your SAB perfectly; otherwise, you will need to buy an oversized piece and trim it down yourself.

The best way to cut acrylic is with either a circular power saw or a jigsaw with a metal cutting blade. If you don't have access to these kinds of tools, you can also use a retractable cutter and a steel ruler to trim the acrylic sheet. A straight line is etched into one side, and the offcut can then be snapped off along the etch by bending it over the edge of the work surface. Although this method does work, it won't produce a very clean cut. Be sure to leave the protective paper coating on while trimming because acrylic scratches easily.

Agar powder

Agar (also called agar-agar) is a gelatinous substance made from algae. It is used in laboratory settings for culturing, and also for culinary purposes as an alternative to gelatin.

Agar powder can be sourced from medical-supply outlets, mushroom cultivation specialists, health or whole food outlets, Asian supermarkets, or online markets.

Although we intend to use agar for culturing and cloning, we don't actually need laboratory-grade agar. A small amount of research will show you that laboratory or bacteriological-grade agar is usually prohibitively expensive. Food-grade agar for use in cooking is perfect for our needs, and is far more affordable.

Food-grade agar can be purchased as dried strips or in powder form. Asian supermarkets often stock both kinds. Strips of dried agar can be powdered in a coffee grinder or blender.

Flow Hood Materials

There are a number of options to research when considering a flow hood. The most painless option is to buy a preassembled unit from a mushroom cultivation specialist as their prices will probably be the lowest for this kind of equipment; however, you should still expect to pay anywhere from five hundred to a thousand dollars or more. Flow hoods can also be purchased from businesses that specialize in providing air-filtration equipment to industry. In this case, you will be looking at equipment designed for use in laboratories, the food industry, and manufacturing. This equipment will be a step up not only in quality, but also in price. You can expect an entry point at around $1,500–$2,000 for this kind of equipment.

When you're building your own flow hood, the major challenges are finding a HEPA filter and a matching centrifugal blower or fan. All other materials for the housing should be easy to find at a hardware store.

When searching for a HEPA filter, look for a business specializing in air-filtration supplies. Then, within their product categories, look for filters designed for use in clean rooms, precision-assembly areas, and clean air/flow hood–type equipment. You can expect to pay a hundred to two hundred fifty dollars or more, depending on filter size.

Blowers or fans can be sourced from suppliers of heating, ventilation, and air-conditioning equipment. These places may even have secondhand equipment at reduced prices. Also, hydroponics shops will stock a range of fans. You should expect to pay between $150 to $400 for a blower/fan, depending on its size and power.

Mushroom cultivation specialists will usually stock the right kind of HEPA filters and blowers as separate items for people who want to make their own flow hood. Buying from specialists will minimize the need for research.

Online markets are another avenue to investigate. You can often find HEPA filters and blowers for considerably less in online markets than anywhere else.

Prefilter material can be purchased from the same air-filtration specialist businesses that stock HEPA filters or businesses involved in air-conditioning/ heating systems. They will stock prefilter material that can be purchased by the meter or in precut pieces. Alternatively, framed filters designed to slide into air-conditioning units and furnaces can also be adapted for use as a flow-hood prefilter.

Gypsum (calcium sulfate dihydrate—CaSO4 2H2O)
Gypsum is purchased from gardening stores or agricultural supply stores. It is usually available in 20–25 kg bags or by the cubic meter. One 25 kg bag will provide you with gypsum for many growing cycles, as each cycle only requires a relatively small amount.

Manure
Horse, cow, chicken, or sheep manure can be sourced in bags from nurseries, gardening stores, or agricultural supply stores. Another alternative is to collect manure yourself, which may be a simple matter if you live in a rural setting, but more difficult if you live in an urban area. For our purposes, manure should be aged and dried, not fresh. A tip for finding horse manure is to look for stables in your area that might allow you to come and collect some. Urban or suburban areas will have horse-racing tracks, equestrian centers, or horse-riding schools, all of which will have stables. Your local police may even have a mounted branch in which they, too, will have stables. Simply call any of these places and ask if they allow members of the public to come and collect manure. You won't be the first person to have contacted them and asked, and they may have specific times of day when they allow access.

Plastic Sheeting
Thick plastic sheeting is used to line the fruiting chamber before spawning to bulk. We prefer tough sheeting that doesn't tear easily and is opaque in order to prevent light from reaching the sides and bottom of the substrate. Suitable plastic sheeting might be found in either the painting or building section of your hardware store. It's usually sold as drop sheets for painters, or as a building material to act a moisture barrier in construction. Avoid very thin, semitransparent sheeting because it will tear easily. Tough plastic sheeting specifically for construction may sometimes be referred to as *builder's film*, and is perfect for our needs.

Pressure Cooker or Canner
For our purposes, we are interested in stove-top pressure cookers or canners large enough for preserving batches of food in jars or cans. A large pressure canner in the range of 20–30 L (21–32 qt) is most suitable for our needs. The pressure cooker/canner must have a pressure gauge to allow monitoring of internal pressure to ensure the cooker is operated at 15 psi for adequate

sterilization.

Depending on where you are in the world, buying a pressure cooker/canner may be as simple as driving to your local supermarket or shopping center and looking around the homewares section. Alternatively, if your local stores don't stock this item, you will need to purchase it online. Online marketplaces certainly have them, as do many mushroom cultivation specialists and independent online retailers. The pressure cooker/canner is one of the pricier items you will need to buy, but it is absolutely essential.

Silicone (RTV)

Silicone that is designed to withstand high temperatures is used when customizing our spawn jar lids. RTV silicone (room temperature vulcanization silicone) can be purchased from automotive retail shops, hardware stores, and online markets. RTV silicone is usually graded to withstand temperatures up to about 200°C (390°F), which is easily sufficient for our needs, given that temperatures inside the pressure cooker reach about 120°C (250°F).

You might come across heat-resistant silicone in canisters designed to be dispensed from a plunger gun. Avoid these products in favor of small tubes with screw-on nozzles, as the large canisters can be unwieldy for our purposes.

Spawn Bags

Spawn bags can be purchased from mushroom cultivation specialists or from online markets. They are usually available with filter patches rated at either 0.2 or 0.5 μm. The latter are recommended because the larger pore size allows for higher rates of GE.

Spore Prints

Spore prints can be purchased from mushroom cultivation specialists. By researching online, you should be able to find numerous commercial options, many of which will ship internationally. Note that the viable spore prints sold by mushroom cultivation outlets are marketed for use in microscopy, not for growing. What you use them for is entirely your choice; however, be aware of the legality of growing psilocybin mushrooms in your location.

Syringes

Empty syringes are needed for making spore syringes. Usually, 20 to 25 mL syringes are preferable because they hold enough spore solution to allow multiple inoculations with one syringe. Empty syringes can be obtained from online markets, veterinary suppliers, and agricultural supply stores that stock products for livestock farming. You may also find them at pet supply stores.

Tyvek Sleeves

Tyvek sleeves can be obtained from online retailers, online markets, and mushroom cultivation specialists. They can be purchased economically in boxes of one hundred, or you should be able to find a retailer that sells them in smaller quantities as well. One pair of sleeves will last a long time. Tyvek sleeves can be cleaned between uses by putting them in the pressure cooker.

WBS

WBS can be purchased economically in large 20-kg bags from pet supply stores. You can also find it at the supermarket; however, it will usually come in smaller bags and is likely to be more expensive. Try to avoid brands that use antifungal treatments. The product label should tell you if the grain has been treated.

8.2 UNIT CONVERSION GUIDES

Centimeters (cm) to Inches (in)

Cm	Inch	Cm	Inch	Cm	Inch	Cm	Inch
1	0.39	26	10.24	51	20.08	76	29.92
2	0.79	27	10.63	52	20.47	77	30.31
3	1.18	28	11.02	53	20.87	78	30.71
4	1.57	29	11.42	54	21.26	79	31.10
5	1.97	30	11.81	55	21.65	80	31.50
6	2.36	31	12.20	56	22.05	81	31.89
7	2.76	32	12.60	57	22.44	82	32.28
8	3.15	33	12.99	58	22.83	83	32.68
9	3.54	34	13.39	59	23.23	84	33.07
10	3.94	35	13.78	60	23.62	85	33.46
11	4.33	36	14.17	61	24.02	86	33.86
12	4.72	37	14.57	62	24.41	87	34.25
13	5.12	38	14.96	63	24.80	88	34.65
14	5.51	39	15.35	64	25.20	89	35.04
15	5.91	40	15.75	65	25.59	90	35.43
16	6.30	41	16.14	66	25.98	100	39.37
17	6.69	42	16.54	67	26.38	125	49.21
18	7.09	43	16.93	68	26.77	150	59.06
19	7.48	44	17.32	69	27.17	175	68.90
20	7.87	45	17.72	70	27.56	200	78.74
21	8.27	46	18.11	71	27.95	250	98.43
22	8.66	47	18.50	72	28.35	300	118.11
23	9.06	48	18.90	73	28.74	500	196.85
24	9.45	49	19.29	74	29.13	750	295.28
25	9.84	50	19.69	75	29.53	1000	393.70

Celsius (°C) to Fahrenheit (°F)

°C	°F	°C	°F	°C	°F	°C	°F
-20	-4	21	69.8	46	114.8	80	176
-15	5	22	71.6	47	116.6	90	194
-10	14	23	73.4	48	118.4	100	212
-5	23	24	75.2	49	120.2	110	230
0	32	25	77	50	122	120	248
1	33.8	26	78.8	51	123.8	130	266
2	35.6	27	80.6	52	125.6	140	284
3	37.4	28	82.4	53	127.4	150	302
4	39.2	29	84.2	54	129.2	160	320
5	41	30	86	55	131	170	338
6	42.8	31	87.8	56	132.8	180	356
7	44.6	32	89.6	57	134.6	190	374
8	46.4	33	91.4	58	136.4	200	392
9	48.2	34	93.2	59	138.2	210	410
10	50	35	95	60	140	220	428
11	51.8	36	96.8	61	141.8	230	446
12	53.6	37	98.6	62	143.6	240	464
13	55.4	38	100.4	63	145.4	250	482
14	57.2	39	102.2	64	147.2	260	500
15	59	40	104	65	149	270	518
16	60.8	41	105.8	66	150.8	280	536
17	62.6	42	107.6	67	152.6	290	554
18	64.4	43	109.4	68	154.4	300	572
19	66.2	44	111.2	69	156.2	350	662
20	68	45	113	70	158	400	752

Liters (L) to Quarts (qt) (US)

Liter	Quart	Liter	Quart	Liter	Quart	Liter	Quart
1	1.06	26	27.47	51	53.89	76	80.31
2	2.11	27	28.53	52	54.95	77	81.36
3	3.17	28	29.59	53	56.00	78	82.42
4	4.23	29	30.64	54	57.06	79	83.48
5	5.28	30	31.70	55	58.12	80	84.54
6	6.34	31	32.76	56	59.17	81	85.59
7	7.40	32	33.81	57	60.23	82	86.65
8	8.45	33	34.87	58	61.29	83	87.71
9	9.51	34	35.93	59	62.34	84	88.76
10	10.57	35	36.98	60	63.40	85	89.82
11	11.62	36	38.04	61	64.46	86	90.88
12	12.68	37	39.10	62	65.51	87	91.93
13	13.74	38	40.15	63	66.57	88	92.99
14	14.79	39	41.21	64	67.63	89	94.05
15	15.85	40	42.27	65	68.68	90	95.10
16	16.91	41	43.32	66	69.74	100	105.67
17	17.96	42	44.38	67	70.80	125	132.09
18	19.02	43	45.44	68	71.85	150	158.50
19	20.08	44	46.49	69	72.91	175	184.92
20	21.13	45	47.55	70	73.97	200	211.34
21	22.19	46	48.61	71	75.02	250	264.17
22	23.25	47	49.66	72	76.08	300	317.01
23	24.30	48	50.72	73	77.14	500	528.34
24	25.36	49	51.78	74	78.19	750	792.52
25	26.42	50	52.83	75	79.25	1000	1056.69

Cubic Meters per Hour (m3/h) to Cubic Foot per Minute (cfm)

cubic meters/hr (m³h)	cubic foot/min (CFM)	cubic meters/hr (m³h)	cubic foot/min (CFM)	cubic meters/hr (m³h)	cubic foot/min (CFM)
300	176.57	550	323.72	800	470.86
310	182.46	560	329.60	810	476.75
320	188.34	570	335.49	820	482.63
330	194.23	580	341.38	830	488.52
340	200.12	590	347.26	840	494.41
350	206.00	600	353.15	850	500.29
360	211.89	610	359.03	860	506.18
370	217.77	620	364.92	870	512.06
380	223.66	630	370.80	880	517.95
390	229.55	640	376.69	890	523.83
400	235.43	650	382.58	900	529.72
410	241.32	660	388.46	910	535.61
420	247.20	670	394.35	920	541.49
430	253.09	680	400.23	930	547.38
440	258.97	690	406.12	940	553.26
450	264.86	700	412.00	950	559.15
460	270.75	710	417.89	960	565.03
470	276.63	720	423.78	970	570.92
480	282.52	730	429.66	980	576.81
490	288.40	740	435.55	990	582.69
500	294.29	750	441.43	1000	588.58
510	300.17	760	447.32	1010	594.46
520	306.06	770	453.20	1020	600.35
530	311.95	780	459.09	1030	606.24
540	317.83	790	464.98	1040	612.12

Pascal (Pa) to Inch Water Column (iwc)

Pascal (Pa)	Inch Water Column (inch wc)	Pascal (Pa)	Inch Water Column (inch wc)	Pascal (Pa)	Inch Water Column (inch wc)
100	0.401	225	0.903	350	1.405
105	0.422	230	0.923	355	1.425
110	0.442	235	0.943	360	1.445
115	0.462	240	0.964	365	1.465
120	0.482	245	0.984	370	1.485
125	0.502	250	1.004	375	1.505
130	0.522	255	1.024	380	1.526
135	0.542	260	1.044	385	1.546
140	0.562	265	1.064	390	1.566
145	0.582	270	1.084	395	1.586
150	0.602	275	1.104	400	1.606
155	0.622	280	1.124	405	1.626
160	0.642	285	1.144	410	1.646
165	0.662	290	1.164	415	1.666
170	0.682	295	1.184	420	1.686
175	0.703	300	1.204	425	1.706
180	0.723	305	1.224	430	1.726
185	0.743	310	1.245	435	1.746
190	0.763	315	1.265	440	1.766
195	0.783	320	1.285	445	1.787
200	0.803	325	1.305	450	1.807
205	0.823	330	1.325	455	1.827
210	0.843	335	1.345	460	1.847
215	0.863	340	1.365	465	1.867
220	0.883	345	1.385	470	1.887

MAGIC MUSHROOM CULTIVATION
Timeline

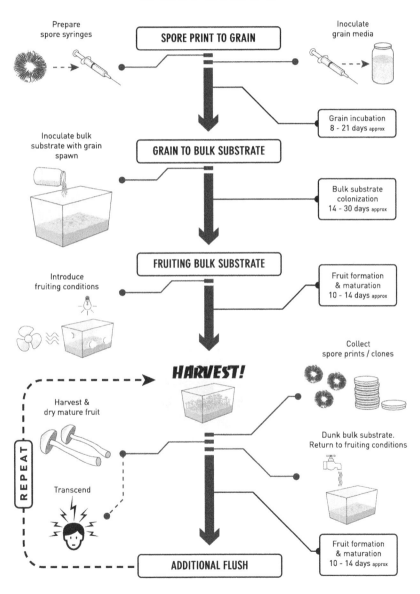

Prepare
spore syringes

Inoculate
grain media

SPORE PRINT TO GRAIN

Grain incubation
8 - 21 days approx

Inoculate bulk
substrate with grain
spawn

GRAIN TO BULK SUBSTRATE

Bulk substrate
colonization
14 - 30 days approx

Introduce
fruiting conditions

FRUITING BULK SUBSTRATE

Fruit formation
& maturation
10 - 14 days approx

Collect
spore prints / clones

HARVEST!

Harvest &
dry mature fruit

Dunk bulk substrate.
Return to fruiting conditions

REPEAT

Transcend

Fruit formation
& maturation
10 - 14 days approx

ADDITIONAL FLUSH

www.magicmushroomgrowguide.com

Index

Y

Made in the USA
Columbia, SC
10 February 2021